CRYSTALS OF LIFE

TITLE II

ROBERT KRASKE

CRYSTALS OF LIFE

The Story of Salt

DOUBLEDAY & COMPANY, INC., GARDEN CITY, NEW YORK

For Steven, Philip, Lisa, and Jan

ACKNOWLEDGMENTS

Readers of this book will discover that salt is a vast subject. Researching it required the generous assistance of many people: librarians in public and university libraries, specialists in agencies of the federal government, and, perhaps most essential, engineers, salesmen, researchers, and administrators in salt companies.

In particular, I should like to thank C. Ramon Greenwood, Morton Salt Company, Chicago; Hamilton Winslow, International Salt Company, Clarks Summit, Pennsylvania; Herbert T. Perkins of Selvage and Lee, Inc., representing the Salt Institute of Chicago; and A. W. Werry, Leslie Salt Company, San Francisco. A special thanks, too, to Mrs. Leslie Nassau and Dr. Thomas G. Aylesworth, Doubleday & Company, Inc., who helped give form to this book.

The section on salt conditions in the Confederacy during the Civil War (Chapter 4) is based on *Salt as a Factor in the Confederacy* by Ella Lonn, University of Alabama Press, 1965. Miss Lonn's book is a valuable reference on a little-known aspect of that war.

Material quoted on pages 74–75 is reprinted from *The Register of the Kentucky Historical Society*, LXIV (1966), and used with permission.

Contents

CRYSTALS OF LIFE

CHAPTER 1

So Universal,
So Necessary to Life...

In 1882, while traveling in British East Africa, a tourist was approached by a native. Behind him stood a grinning fourteen-year-old girl.

Would *bwana* care to buy his daughter, he asked. She would make a fine servant. He held out her arm for the man to inspect. "Strong," the tribesman said. "No sickness. Good worker."

When the tourist tried to edge aside, the native grabbed his arm. "Cheap," he urged. "Only four loaves salt!"

In central Africa a century ago, human life was so abundant and salt so scarce that, from the Red Sea to the Atlantic coast, men, women, and children were sold into slavery for a few handfuls of the precious stuff.

Today we do not value salt and human life in the same terms. But, since man first existed on earth, life and salt have been interrelated in ways few people realize.

Like air and water, salt is a basic necessity of life. Bathing the billions of cells that make up each of our bodies is the interstitial fluid, a solution that contains three ounces of salt, about half a cupful.

Sometimes you can taste this salt in blood from a cut or in your tears and sweat. This salty fluid is essential to life: it helps maintain the delicate chemical balances of our bodies. Deprive a man or animal of salt and the result is certain: he dies.

Because man's life depends on it, salt has always played a vital role in his affairs. In fact, no other mineral has occupied such an important place in his everyday living from ancient times to the present.

Today salt is even more important in our lives than ever before. Not only are we dependent on salt for life, but modern industry is dependent on salt to manufacture the goods we use in daily living.

A close-up of a cluster of solar-salt crystals. *Leslie Salt Company*

For all its importance in our lives, salt is a rather un-complicated material. A mineral found both underground and in the sea, it is composed of two elements in equal shares: sodium and chlorine.

Sodium is a reactive metal. It combines or reacts easily with many other elements. Chlorine is a poisonous gas. When they combine, a change comes over these two elements: they become harmless and they harden into a white cubical crystal.

This is a modern definition of salt. But long before we used chemical analysis to determine what salt was composed of, men were content simply to marvel at this wondrous substance.

In 1584, a French writer named Jean de Marcounille wrote: "This mineral is like unto the four elements—earth, air, fire, and water. So universal, so necessary to life, it is the fifth element!"

This is the story of salt, the amazing universal mineral. It begins long before man appeared on earth and it spans man's history up to the present day.

VALUABLE AND SACRED

In the ancient world, men regarded salt as a valuable—even a sacred—substance. Customs and superstitions were developed around salt; people all over the world made it a part of their religious ceremonies. In Europe, Africa, and across Asia to China, it was even used as money.

Visiting China in the thirteenth century, the Venetian traveler Marco Polo wrote this about the inhabitants of one province: "They have none of the Great Khan's paper money, but use salt instead of money."

Salt makers in this province, he discovered, molded salt

into half-pound lumps shaped like cups—flat on top, round on the bottom. They used these lumps, Polo wrote, as "small change."

In another province, he saw flat cakes of salt inscribed with the stamp of the Great Khan, like our coins today imprinted with the profiles of Presidents.

But even hundreds of years before Marco Polo visited China, people in other countries were using salt as money.

In 1500 B.C., Egyptians made salt "coins" eight inches long, four inches wide, and two and a half inches thick.

Twenty centuries ago, armed Roman soldiers guarded the Via Salaria—Salt Road—along which ox carts hauled valuable salt 150 miles from the seacoast town of Ostia where it was produced to the world's capital city, Rome.

Caesar's troops received part of their pay in salt. Salt money was called *salarium,* from which we now have the word "salary." The phrase "not worth his salt" probably was first applied to lazy soldiers who did not earn their salt.

In many areas, salt was valued more highly than human life. The early Greeks bought slaves and paid for them with their salt "coins." But the slave trade in salt was most widely practiced in central Africa.

The grassy plains of central Africa lacked salt streams and swamps. To bring salt to village markets, long files of porters, human packtrains, carried loads of salt on their heads on a six-month journey from the Red Sea.

"A brick of salt, the load of a light porter, is the price of a slave among them," wrote a nineteenth-century explorer. "The brother sells his sister, the husband his wife, for salt." Parents sold their children, too.

In Africa, a man could buy a bride for ten five-pound cylinders of salt, wrapped in palm leaves, paid to the girl's father.

The use of salt as money has continued into the twentieth century. Just before World War II began, Italian troops invaded Ethiopia. Soldiers broke into the government's vaults and found bars of salt neatly stacked. Like our gold bullion stored at Fort Knox, the salt was part of that African nation's financial reserve.

During World War II, pilots flying over China carried a pound or two of salt in their escape kits along with a million yen of Chinese money. The salt was a wise precaution: if they were downed, the fliers could use the salt to buy help from people in remote areas where salt was scarce and prized even more than money.

NATURE'S PRESERVATIVE

While he still lived in caves and hunted his food with stone-tipped spears, man discovered two of salt's most useful properties: it preserves meat from decay and it brings out the flavor of food.

Salt is nature's own preservative. Its attraction for water draws moisture from micro-organisms in meat that cause decay; the moisture flows to a coating of salt put on the meat. Deprived of moisture, the bacteria die, and thus the meat is prevented from spoiling.

Other means of keeping meat fresh have been developed since early man discovered salt's natural preservative powers. But around the world salt is still the most widely used food preservative.

Along with incense and spices, salt was a major item of commerce in the ancient world. Trade in salt determined the routes of the first highways and sea lanes; the Phoenicians, for instance, sailed the length of the Mediterranean Sea to quarry salt in Spain. Along these land and sea routes, men built cities. One city built on a salt route is the hub of England today: London.

DEAR TO THE GODS

Throughout history, man has accorded few of earth's materials the reverence he has reserved for salt.

Before meals, the Greeks prayerfully offered it to their gods. It was, they believed, "dear to the gods." At harvest

Nine-inch-long, gold, enamel, and pearl saltcellar made by Benvenuto Cellini. *The Metropolitan Museum of Art, Bequest of Benjamin Altman, 1913*

time, the Hebrews presented salt to Jehovah. Salt is mentioned thirty-two times in the King James Version of the Holy Bible, as in "Ye are the salt of the earth."

Indians in the Western Hemisphere believed in the sacred power of salt. One of the four Aztec deities was a salt goddess. American Navaho Indians prayed to "Salt Woman." The Hopis revered "Salt Man" as their war god.

Customs and superstitions have always surrounded salt. On tables of European royalty, salt was honored by being placed in valuable bowls and cups like the hammered-gold Rospigliosi cup pictured in these pages. The cup was made in the sixteenth century by the master Italian craftsman, Benvenuto Cellini.

At royal banquets, guests quickly learned their standing with their host, the king, by their position at the table "above or below the salt." Those nobles seated "below the salt" realized they had little favor in court.

Anyone who accidentally spilled salt knew he was in for a spell of bad luck—and not only on earth. Dire punishment awaited him in the hereafter as well.

The English believed that for every grain spilled a tear would be shed in sorrow. Another widespread belief had the spiller waiting outside the gates of Paradise for as many years as there were grains spilled.

Beliefs in salt's supernatural powers continue in parts of the world to this day.

In backward regions of Russia, peasants place salt in the coffins of their dead in the belief that it will preserve them in the hereafter.

In the Far East, mothers rub new-born babies with salt to assure their good health. And small children wear bags of salt on strings around their necks to guard against the "evil eye."

Man has also used salt as a symbol of trust. In Near

A detail from Leonardo da Vinci's "The Last Supper." In the full painting, Jesus has just announced, "One of you shall betray me." An angry Peter leans over to John. "Who is it?" he asks. Judas Iscariot, startled by Jesus' words, knocks over a saltcellar. The spilled salt is an omen of the ill fortune that now awaits him. *The Bettmann Archive*

Eastern countries, no person taking part in an agreement sanctified with salt would dare violate it. In the deserts of Arabia, men from different tribes began a conference by placing salted bread in each other's mouths. "By this salt and bread," they chanted, "I will not betray thee!"

In 1857, after a century of careless rule by the British, 230,000 Indian troops in the British Army revolted against their masters—all, that is, except a handful of troops who had "sworn by their salt" to serve the British crown. Because of their sacred oath, these Indian troops actually fought against their own people to put down the revolt.

HARDSHIPS AND 14,000 USES

While man has honored salt, he has also suffered hardships and fought wars over it. Salt played a part in the bloody French Revolution. In the first century A.D., two German tribes called the Chatti and Mermanduri clashed with spears and battle-axes over a salt-bearing stream. Thousands of warriors lost their lives for this prize.

A lack of salt contributed to the disastrous defeat of Napoleon's Grand Army in its invasion of Russia, and the American Civil War saw the South's war effort slowed by blundering mismanagement of salt.

So necessary is salt in war that, if a modern nation declared war without enormous stores of salt on hand, it might just as well try to fight without guns.

We tend to regard salt today as having only one purpose: to flavor our food. Actually, only five out of every hundred pounds of salt produced in the United States today find their way to our dinner tables either in salt shakers or as the flavoring that food companies add to meats and canned vegetables. Industry has found so many uses for those other ninety-five pounds that no one has ever tried to count them. Most estimates peg the number of uses at 14,000!

"Where do we sell it?" said a salt salesman in a large industrial city. "See those factories out there?" From the window of his twenty-second-story office, he pointed to a broad section of the city spotted with the smoking chimneys of factories. *"That's* where we sell salt!"

Merely to list all the ways man uses salt today would require, at twenty-five items per page, a book 560 pages thick. The pages would list uses ranging from dandruff removal to cooling nuclear reactors. Later we will detail this astonishing variety of ways man has found to use salt.

But for now, consider this: nearly everything you can see about you at this moment—including the paper and ink in this book and the clothes you are wearing—used salt in its manufacture. Without salt, the wheels of industry would slow to a halt.

Fortunately, man is not likely to run out of this indispensable natural resource. Under the surface of most of the world's countries lie salt deposits containing billions of tons of the mineral.

And dissolved in the depths of the oceans are additional vast stores of salt. In only two cubic miles of ocean there is enough salt to build a wall equal in length and mass to the 1500-mile-long Great Wall of China—and still have enough salt left over for an additional five hundred miles of wall!

Scientists estimate that if all the oceans suddenly dried up and the salt were shoveled up on the United States, our country would be buried under a salt blanket one and a half miles deep. Only a few peaks of the Rocky Mountain range would poke through the surface.

And yet, with all earth's immense stores of salt, there

are people in countries today who treasure salt by the handful. They produce their precious supply in ways their ancestors used hundreds of years ago, (which is not so strange perhaps when you realize that salt is produced commercially in the United States today by the same methods the Chinese used four thousand years ago). For these people, salt hunger—the absence of salt in the diet—is a serious threat.

"We may conclude then—by Hercules!—that the higher enjoyments of life could not exist today without the use of salt"—a statement far more true today than when a Roman naturalist named Pliny the Elder wrote it nearly two thousand years ago.

THE CATHEDRAL OF SALT

One of the modern wonders of the world is hidden underground in a salt mine in the Andes Mountains forty miles north of Bogotá, Colombia.

A half-mile down inside the salt mountain of Zipitquirá stands a majestic cathedral four hundred feet long, as large as Paris' famed Cathedral of Notre Dame. Its walls, its ceiling, the great cross standing on the altar are all hewn out of solid rock salt. Spaced along the walls are ten side altars with salt figures representing scenes from the Bible.

Worshipers enter the cathedral, which opened for worship on Christmas Eve 1952, by trooping down a half-mile-long slope cut into the mountainside. Each year, two hundred thousand persons visit the cathedral.

The craggy walls of rock salt rise seventy feet in dim light to the vaulted ceiling. The air is dry and cool; there is a feeling of awe, of timelessness, of reverence. From

The Salt Cathedral of Zipitquirá near Bogotá, Colombia. The angel on the pedestal at right and the altar in the background are carved out of rock salt. *Colombia National Tourist Board*

these galleries, primitive men—the ancestors of us all—hacked out life-giving salt. The mine was old before the Spaniards conquered the land four hundred years ago. In later years, salt from this mine helped produce the material things that make up modern civilization.

CHAPTER 2

When the Earth Was Young

Where did salt come from in the first place? How did it get into the ocean or buried a thousand feet underground?

To answer these questions, we must go back billions of years to the time when the earth was created.

Many geologists believe that when the earth was first formed it was solid rock. There were no men or animals about, no plants, no water. Only rock, hard and hot.

As heat rose from the young earth, it caused water vapor in the air to form clouds. Thick and black, they covered the entire earth, blotting out the sun. And from these clouds onto the dark earth, rain began to fall.

At first, the rain was changed into steam as it touched the superheated earth. Then, as the earth cooled, the rain ran in rivulets over the wet rocks into pools, and the pools overflowed and became streams. This ancient rain may have fallen for a million years.

Under the rain's steady drumming, the rock began wearing away. Minerals in the rocks—including grains of sodium chloride, table salt—broke loose and washed away in streams. The streams became rivers that wound their way to the low places on earth, to the vast deeps between the continents that today are filled with the oceans.

It is believed that each year during this centuries-long

Ancient rains washed away salt embedded in rocks into streams to the ocean. The washing away of salt from rock continues to this day. This photograph was taken recently in Arizona. *Bureau of Reclamation, U. S. Department of the Interior*

The world's largest building, in terms of cubic feet, is the fifty-two-story Vertical Assembly Building at Florida's Cape Kennedy. In this building, America's giant space rockets are assembled in an upright stance. The VAB is so cavernous that the United Nations Building could be rolled through one of its 456-foot-high doors. Yet it would take twenty VABs to contain the salt in one cubic mile of ocean water. *National Aeronautics and Space Administration*

rain about 6500 cubic miles of water flowed into the oceans, about five times the annual flow of the Mississippi River into the Gulf of Mexico.

As a result of this early downpour, 70% of the earth's surface is today covered by ocean water. The total volume of water in the ocean amounts to 320 million cubic miles. And dissolved in each cubic mile of ocean are 166 million tons of salt, the same salt that originally was embedded in the rocks of the young earth.

How big a pile would 166 million tons of salt make? The largest of the Great Pyramids of Egypt—Cheops—is one of the bulkiest man-made structures ever built. It measures 755 feet on each side of its base, rises 450 feet, and spreads over thirteen acres of desert. Yet the salt in a single cubic mile of ocean would make twenty-eight pyramids the size of Cheops!

And all the salt in the ocean? How can we visualize that?

The Encyclopaedia Britannica puts it this way: ". . . if dried up, the entire ocean would yield no less than 4,500,-000 cubic miles of rock salt—or about 14½ times the bulk of the entire continent of Europe above high water."

BURIED SALT

Even today, the washing away of salt from the rocky continents continues. Geologists estimate that the Rio Grande deposits nearly four tons of salt in the Gulf of Mexico each *minute*—5600 tons every day—the equivalent of a hundred-boxcar train of salt dumped into the ocean daily from this one river alone.

The oceans were also the source of the salt that today is dug from mines a thousand feet underground.

Three to five hundred million years ago, the earth went through a process of violent change. In places, the surface of the earth split and whole mountain ranges thrust upward, some from the bottom of the sea. One such upheaval separated what we now call the Dead Sea from the Mediterranean Sea.

During this period of violent change, vast lakes of sea water were trapped by rising rock walls. The water stood

Air view of salt bed at Searles Lake, California. This photo suggests how ancient seas, landlocked by surrounding mountains, evaporated and left behind a bed of salt. *American Potash and Chemical Corporation*

quietly while from above the sun beat down. Centuries passed, and gradually the water evaporated and left behind a bed of salt.

One of these landlocked seas covered parts of Utah, Nevada, and Montana with a salty lake the size of Lake Michigan. But all that remains of this ancient sea today is the twenty-by-eighty-mile Great Salt Lake. Thousands of

years ago, an earthquake opened a gap in the mountain
range surrounding the lake. The water drained through the
gap and to the Pacific Ocean by way of the Snake and
Columbia Rivers.

When the water level dropped below the gap, the lake
was again landlocked. However, streams from surrounding
mountains continued to feed salt into the lake. Today the
waters of the Great Salt Lake carry an estimated six billion
tons of salt.

Other ancient salt lakes were also victims of earthquakes.
Cracks opened in their floors and the water drained into
cavities deep in the earth. When the earth shifted again,
rocks exerted pressure on these cavities filled with salt
water. The pressure caused the water to escape through

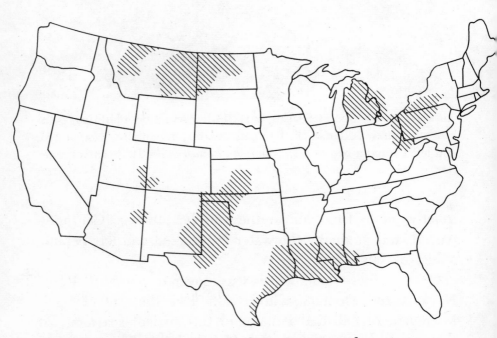

Major underground deposits of salt in America today.

cracks and fissures in the surrounding rock. Through cracks that ran to the surface, the salt water emerged as brine springs. These springs exist today in eastern North America, in Asia, and in Central Europe.

Besides the Utah-Nevada-Montana area, two other sections of the United States were covered by ancient seas. The largest sea, a hundred thousand square miles in area, spread over parts of Kansas, Oklahoma, and Texas. The second, in the East, covered a seventy thousand square mile area that is now Michigan, Ontario, Ohio, West Virginia, Pennsylvania, and New York.

Geologists believe that this eastern sea was separated from the ocean by a narrow bar of land. The bar was low; ocean waves swept over it and poured into the trapped sea. The water in this sea had no outlet and over thousands of years it evaporated, again leaving salt behind in amounts that stagger the imagination.

In places, salt built up in deposits a third of a mile thick. In Michigan alone, the ancient sea left behind seventy-one trillion tons of salt in a great saucer underlying nearly all the southern half of the state.

This immense salt deposit was made over three hundred million years ago, fifty million years before dinosaurs began roaming the land.

A FAR-OFF RUMBLING

Once the ancient landlocked seas had disappeared, vast deserts of salt lay glittering in the sun. If there was any sound at all in this cold, lifeless world, it was only the dry rustle of salt grains shifting to and fro as the wind sighed across the empty wastes.

But one day there came a far-off rumbling and each day it grew louder.

Glacier!

In the distance, advancing, swallowing boulders the size of houses and grinding them to pebbles, was a wall of ice perhaps two miles high. So heavy was this ice shield that, in America, it gouged out the valleys now filled with the water of the Great Lakes.

Over the past million years alone, at least four glaciers advanced across America, Europe, and Asia toward the equator and ground over the beds of salt. As each glacier melted, it deposited a layer of rock and soil hundreds of feet thick on the salt.

After the last glacier melted, the salt in what is now Michigan lay buried 1800 feet down. In Ohio, two thousand feet of earth covered the salt.

The earth-crushing weight of the ice pressed the salt grains together into rock, hence the name "rock salt." A pickaxe struck at a salt wall in a mine today will barely chip it, so tightly have the grains been fused by the pressure of earth and glaciers over it.

SALT DOMES

In the South, the process of depositing underground salt beds was different. Along the rim of the Gulf of Mexico, from Alabama to the southern tip of Texas, the salt lies close to the surface, a scant twenty feet down at Avery Island, Louisiana.

The salt deposits in this area demonstrate another geologic process—the titanic forces involved in earth movements, the constant shifting and readjusting of the earth's rocky crust, and its effect on salt beds.

About the time the salt deposits in the North were made, salt was also deposited in flat beds along the coast of the Gulf of Mexico. Up to this time, the process was the same as that in the North: bodies of sea water trapped behind sand bars or rocky cliffs, slow evaporation, and salt left behind.

But in the South the process then changed. No glaciers crawled to the Gulf Coast to bury the salt under thousands of feet of sediment. Instead, by a geologic quirk not fully understood—perhaps by repeated earthquakes of awesome size that caused land masses around the Gulf Coast to sink —the salt beds gradually sank deeper into the earth under a covering of thousands of feet of rock, in places, thirty to fifty thousand feet thick.

Then the salt began rising. Under the enormous dead-weight pressure of the six to ten miles of rock above it, the salt was compressed from its normal solid state into a slowly flowing plastic mass.

The salt pressed through a fault line in the rock layer above. In time—in the slow motion of millions of years of geologic time—the pressure of the salt bent the rock layer at the fault line and eventually punctured it. Widening the gap, the fluid salt seeped through to the layer above, and then the process was repeated.

As it pushed upward, the salt gradually formed a circular dome, one-half to four miles wide across its flat top. Near the surface, the flat tops of some domes spread like mushroom heads. At one dome, salt drillers penetrated the mushroom overhang to a depth of 2800 feet before breaking into the rock through which the salt had penetrated.

Along the Gulf Coast, 235 of these vertical domes—giant columns of salt—have been located. Geologists estimate that some domes contain five hundred billion tons of salt, although there may even be more because the buried "mother lode" of salt thirty to fifty thousand feet down cannot be surveyed.

Domes like those on our Gulf Coast have also been discovered in Colombia, Germany, Spain, Rumania, North Africa, the Near East, and in Russia.

Around the world, salt had now been deposited in underground beds and in the sea. Earth, no longer young, readied herself for the entrance of her star performer, man. But salt had to come first; it could not have happened the other way around.

CHAPTER 3

The Great Mystery: Why Man Needs Salt

The relationship of salt to life has puzzled man for centuries. One thing we know for certain is that salt is as necessary to our lives as the air we breathe and the water we drink.

In 1684, an English chemist named Robert Boyle was the first to demonstrate the presence of salt in the body. Curious about the salty taste of his blood and sweat, he took a specimen of blood and removed the cells—leaving only the plasma.

"There remained behind," he wrote with enthusiasm and amazement, "salt which was scarce distinguishable from marine salt!"

Investigating Boyle's discovery, physicians in the eighteenth century evaporated human sweat and saliva and found what they called "cubic crystals of sea salt" in the residue.

A century later, physicians were still experimenting with the salt present in the body. Their experiments had progressed to examining the fluids around the lungs, heart, brain, and spine. Salt was "the principal inorganic constituent" of these fluids, they announced. Furthermore, "the main inorganic material in blood serum is sodium chloride"—common salt.

SALT HUNGER

Building on these findings by earlier scientists, modern medical researchers have discovered that, to maintain the proper amount of salt in his body, an adult of average size and weight must take in six grams each day, about a thimbleful. Infants require one gram; children, three grams.

About half of our daily requirement comes from salt we add for flavoring to our food. The other half is already present in the meat and vegetables we eat and in the water we drink.

Most people today have no problem getting their daily salt ration. But history is spotted with pitiful tales of salt hunger.

A century ago in central Africa where salt is scarce, people drank the blood and urine of cattle and wild animals to get the salt their bodies needed. The animals, as they wandered over the plains, obtained salt by feeding on grasses and plants, sources of minute amounts of salt.

Salt hunger has also been used as a weapon for executing criminals. In Holland and Sweden during the Middle Ages, a judge sentencing a criminal to death had the privilege of offering the man a choice: immediate execution or a month in a cell without salt.

Fortunate the criminal who chose immediate execution. The brave but foolish man who chose a month without salt was placed in a cell and fed unsalted bread. He only prolonged the suffering that led to his agonizing death.

What does a prolonged absence of salt in his diet do to a man? How long can he live without salt?

In England some years ago, three college students decided to perform an experiment on themselves. They called it "Salt Hunger: Its Effects on the Human Body."

What would happen, they wanted to find out, if they eliminated all salt from their diet?

The experiment was dangerous, they knew that. Dogs in saltless-diet experiments had survived only three weeks. So they kept a physician on hand. Lucky they did, because without him they might have died.

Their diet consisted of fruit, unsalted bread and butter, and vegetables boiled three times to remove every last trace of salt. Their water was boiled and the steam distilled to remove minute traces of salt.

During the first week, the students lost the salt their bodies held in reserve, chiefly from sweat and urine. Then they began feeling the symptoms of salt hunger. They lost their appetites. Their muscles ached and their breath came in short gasps. They were afflicted with diarrhea and vomiting. They were constantly thirsty.

Even the smallest effort—like shaving, which they soon gave up—exhausted them.

By the beginning of the third week, the experiment had reached a critical stage. Drained of energy, the three young men did nothing all day but sit listlessly in chairs.

At this point, the doctor stopped the experiment. "They were deeply depressed," he reported. "I was afraid they were losing their will to live."

Yet, in some places, there are people who use no salt in their food and do not even have a word for it in their language—the Kirghizes, desert dwellers of Turkestan, for example.

But in their avoidance of salt these people are not exceptions to the human family. They live almost solely on milk and fresh or roasted meat, and their bodies extract the salt they need from these foods.

When the famous explorer Vilhjalmur Stefansson lived with Eskimos above the Arctic Circle between 1913 and 1918, he found that, like his Eskimo hosts, he lost his liking for salt added to his food.

Where did he get the salt his body needed? From the same high-salt foods his Eskimo friends ate: the meat, blood, and organs of seals, walrus, fish, and caribou.

"Apparently," he wrote in a 1944 Arctic survival manual for the U.S. armed services, "all people everywhere in the world who live mainly or solely on meat dislike and avoid salt."

But the rest of mankind appreciates the taste of a pinch of salt added to their food.

SALT AND LIFE

Salt performs vital work in our bodies. It helps maintain the volume of blood and water in our blood vessel systems.

In 1935, a doctor with the National Institute of Public Health discovered that a weak salt-water solution injected directly into the bloodstream can serve as a temporary blood substitute for accident or shock victims. Salt is also essential for the proper functioning of our nerves and muscles.

But salt has a more important function.

Surrounding the billions of cells in our bodies is a salt and water solution that is absolutely essential to life. It is in fact the only environment that will support life. Scientists have found that, if you remove a blood cell from its interstitial fluid and place it in clear water, it will burst!

Why this is so, no one really knows. And the answer may be beyond our reach—in the past, millions of years ago, when life first appeared on earth.

Most scientists believe that the first living cells floated in the warm, salty seas that filled the deep basins between the continents. Long before appearing on land, life in some unknown form thrived in the sea.

Countless millions of years passed before a living creature emerged from the sea onto the dry land. This creature had a spinal column, an organ like a lung that could breathe oxygen, and one other feature that ties him to us: the cells and organs of his body were bathed in a salty fluid not unlike the one that each of us, man and animal alike, carries with him today.

So vital to life is this salty fluid that nature provides us with a mechanism to regulate the salt-to-water balance in our bodies.

A man weighing 150 pounds keeps about three ounces of salt dissolved in his blood and in the interstitial fluid.

A healthy body maintains an exact balance between intake and discharge of salt. Only in extreme circumstances is a man in danger of depleting his body's store of salt. Blast furnace workers, for example, or men who do heavy work in the hot, humid climate of the tropics can sweat out an ounce of salt in an eight-hour day, one-third of their body's supply. These people usually take salt pills the size of aspirin tablets to replace the salt they lose.

When we have extra salt in our bodies—after a heavy meal, for example—the kidneys remove it through urination and the sweat glands are activated.

When our salt supply is low—from sweating on a hot day—the kidneys separate salt out of waste matter and pass it back into our bloodstreams. Salt is then absent from our sweat and urine—almost.

Despite this, salt persists in escaping from our bodies. The kidneys, as they go about cleansing the blood of waste material and water, continue to pass off minute amounts of salt. So do the sweat glands. Even when we cannot feel sweat on our bodies, small amounts of salt, about a hundred milligrams per day, pass through the pores of our skin dissolved in invisible sweat.

As the body's salt level continues to drop, the body discharges water in order to balance the vital proportion of salt to water.

Now the situation is at a crucial point. If the body does not get salt to replace its lost supply, it passes off so much water that it causes its own death—of thirst!

When the body lacks water, just the opposite reaction occurs. To maintain the vital salt-to-water balance, the body begins to pass off salt. If water is not replaced, again the body dies of thirst.

The delicate balance nature requires between salt and water in man's body also explains why sailors adrift in an open boat cannot drink sea water and survive.

Sea water is 3.5% salt, one and one-fourth ounces in every quart. Man's maximum tolerance for salt in water is only 2%. If a sailor drinks sea water, his body immediately reacts: his stomach tries to get rid of it by vomiting. But vomiting removes only part of the salt he has taken in. Now his kidneys start reacting. Triggered into action by excess salt, they try to wash it out with the water in his body. This flushing of the body leads to dehydration—drying out. As a result, he dies of thirst, an agony now made torturous because his body is saturated with salt.

CHAPTER 4

War, Taxes, and Salt

"The King, too, I can assure you, gets a great revenue from this salt," wrote Marco Polo in the thirteenth century after visiting a Chinese province where salt makers pumped brine from deep wells.

Kublai Khan—called "King" by Polo—was not the only ruler in the ancient world who turned man's craving for salt into a source of revenue for his treasury.

Wherever men settled in their first colonies—in the fertile river valleys of China, Egypt, Babylon, India, Mexico, and Peru—rulers decreed that salt was the property of the state and taxed the people for using it. Nor were salt taxes limited to nations in the ancient world. As recently as 1947, the people of India paid a salt tax to the British Government.

But not all people submitted meekly to a salt tax. In Europe between the sixteenth and eighteenth centuries, Frenchmen and Englishmen called the tax unjust and re-sisted paying it. Defying the law, salt runners smuggled salt. They risked harsh penalties—in England, imprisonment and death; in France, torture and forced labor on slave galleys. In sixteenth-century Venice, captured salt smug-glers had one ear cut off.

In 1785, the Earl of Dundonald gave a fiery speech in the British Parliament in which he urged repeal of the salt tax.

"Every year in England," he told the House of Lords, "ten thousand people are seized for salt smuggling!" The burden of the tax falls on the poor, he cried. They cannot pay it and demand reform. He pleaded: "Tax the rich instead!"

Parliament did not listen, and within a few years mobs roamed London streets shouting for the repeal of the tax.

Frightened by the fury of the people, Parliament cut the tax and then, in 1825, abolished it altogether.

Across the English Channel in France, King Louis XVI had inherited a system of salt taxation two hundred years old. Every year over those two centuries, soldiers arrested two to three thousand men and women for salt smuggling.

The salt tax in France was, with Louis' approval, nothing more than wholesale robbery of the poor.

A weak and vain king, Louis followed the practice of his royal ancestors and appointed court favorites as "salt farmers." These salt farmers were often crafty and unscrupulous men. They paid huge bribes to Louis. In return, he granted each of them police control of a certain district. This control allowed them to fix taxes on salt—always high and more than poor peasants could afford.

Taxes collected by the salt farmers allowed them to live in luxurious mansions in Paris or on huge estates in the country. They ordered peasants in their districts to purchase salt from warehouses which they owned. When the peasants bought salt for use on fish or meat to sell in the marketplace, salt left over in the salting process had to be thrown away. For meals, the peasants had to purchase a second supply of salt.

Tanners and leather dressers bought specially treated salt; it was poisoned. The poison had no effect on leather, but it prevented the tanners from using the salt on food.

The salt farmers cracked down hard on smugglers. A

smuggler got off easy if he were only sent to prison or to a slave galley.

For the smuggler repeating his crime, the salt farmers reserved a special punishment. The offender was placed on a ladder called a "rack." His wrists and ankles were tied with a rope that reached over the top and bottom of the rack. The rope was wound around a windlass which, when turned by a crank, stretched his body with excruciating pain. While this was going on, a second torturer shoved a pack of lighted candles into the man's ribs.

The peasants grumbled over the salt tax and the salt farmers, but King Louis chose to ignore them. Only when mobs stormed the Bastille—the state prison in Paris—on July 14, 1789, did he repeal the tax. But by then it was too late.

Once the French Revolution started—ignited in part by the hated salt tax—the merciless salt farmers were among the first to have their heads lopped off by the guillotine!

100,000 PRISONERS

The English, having repealed the salt tax at home, imposed a similar tax on one of the countries they had conquered: India. Even making salt by scooping water up from the sea and allowing it to evaporate was considered a criminal offense. Indians, poor and desperate for salt, took to burning great piles of grass and vegetable greens to get specks of blackened salt in the ashes.

As years passed, the tax became a symbol of foreign tyranny to a man who dreamed of independence for India: Mahatma Gandhi.

To dramatize the injustice of a foreign nation ruling his

country, Gandhi decided to make the English salt tax a national issue.

On March 12, 1930, Gandhi started to walk from Ahmedabad to the seaside village of Dandi, a distance of 241 miles. Seventy-eight men and women fell in behind him.

On April 5, he arrived at the seashore. By this time, ten thousand men, women, and children followed him. Outnumbered police worked frantically to keep the mob in order. On the beach, Gandhi picked up a lump of crystallized salt and tasted it, thus breaking the law.

All along India's three-thousand-mile coastline on that same day, thousands of other Indians picked up salt. The English were befuddled. They began arresting the offenders until their jails held 100,000 people and could hold no more. Still the Indians picked up salt and defied the British rule. But even after this mass protest, the British refused to repeal the salt tax.

One of the few governments in all history that has never imposed a salt tax on its people is the United States Government.

SALT IN WAR

In 1777, during the Revolutionary War when British troops threatened the American Army's store of salt, General Washington wrote an urgent dispatch: "Every attempt must be made to save it!"

Despite Washington's order, the British captured the Americans' supply. To replace the lost salt, our soldiers bought it from farmers at a costly eight dollars per bushel, eight times the peacetime rate.

General Washington paid the price because he knew that

salt was as necessary to his army as guns and gunpowder. It was needed to preserve the soldiers' rations of beef and pork, to tan leather for boots and saddles, and to keep up the strength of the men and horses.

Napoleon's Grand Army, in its invasion of Russia in 1812, lost its salt. The results were tragic.

On September 12, six hundred thousand French soldiers crossed the border into Russia. So swift was their advance that they outran their supply wagons. The victorious French soldiers, deep in Russian territory, suddenly found themselves with only the food they carried in their knapsacks— and the fierce Russian winter coming on.

On October 20, the Grand Army began a thousand-mile retreat across Russia's frozen plains. The temperature dropped to seventeen degrees below zero. Without food, their salt gone, men and horses dropped exhausted.

Disabled soldiers found their wounds would not heal because their bodies lacked salt. Disease spread through the ranks.

By December 3, twenty thousand survivors of the Grand Army straggled out of Russia, defeated by cold, hunger, and lack of salt.

WHY THE NORTH
WHIPPED THE SOUTH

A few years after the Civil War, a southern plantation owner visited relatives on their farm in the North. In their barn he noticed a sack of salt. "Know why you Northeners whipped us Southeners?" he asked. "Because you had this . . ." and he sifted a handful of salt kernels through his fingers.

The plantation owner's startling remark called attention to a little-known drama of the South's war effort. While locked in a death struggle with the North, the South was also fighting a losing battle within its own borders to produce salt for its army and for nine million civilians.

Before the war, southern states produced nearly two and a half million bushels of salt a year, but this was not enough to meet the needs of the people. (The Gulf Coast salt domes were not discovered until the twentieth century.) To supply the demand, southern states imported salt from the North and from Europe.

Consequently, when the war began in 1861 and the Union Navy blockaded southern ports, the South was faced with an immediate salt shortage. From every corner of the Confederacy, the cry went up: "Salt!"—from meat packers who needed it to cure beef and pork; from leather workers who used it to tan leather for harnesses, bridles, saddles, boots, and shoes; from the army which had to have it for soldiers' rations and to feed horses and mules; from munitions makers who used it in manufacturing gunpowder. Lost in the outcry for salt were southern civilians.

Before the war, salt sold in the South for about seventeen cents for a seventy-pound bushel—one-fourth cent a pound. Shortages immediately skyrocketed the price. By November 1862, a bushel cost thirty-five dollars in Richmond, Virginia, the South's capital. At the end of the war, a pound of salt brought five dollars in Georgia—about three hundred fifty dollars per bushel. And captains of schooners that slipped through rings of Union ships blockading southern ports demanded and got twice that price.

Speculators zeroed in on pre-war salt stored in warehouses. Quickly they bought up these supplies and, as the demand soared, resold them at fantastic profits. One shrewd operator bought four thousand dollars' worth of salt in St. Louis, shipped it to Arkansas, and there resold it for $65,000!

By December of that first year of war, southern civilians were desperate for salt. Worried governors warned President Jefferson Davis of an impending salt famine among the people.

Farmers were hardest hit. To preserve meat, they required a hundred pounds of salt for each thousand pounds of beef and about sixty-five pounds of salt for each five hundred pounds of pork.

The unsalted butter that farmers made did not last as long as salted butter in the warm southern climate before turning rancid. They also needed salt to pack eggs, both to keep them fresh by preventing air from penetrating the shells and to protect them against breakage. And without salt, the hides of slaughtered animals simply rotted.

During the war, both farmers and civilians found substitutes for other foodstuffs they were deprived of, like coffee, tea, and sugar. But for salt, they never found an adequate replacement. Farmers tried curing hams and bacon over wood fires until the heat evaporated the moisture. The result was dry and tasteless, but at least edible.

They also tried retrieving salt that had dripped into the dirt under smokehouses from years of curing meats. First they punctured the bottom of a tub with holes. Then they filled the tub with the fatty soil from under the smokehouse and poured water through it. After boiling the brine that dripped through, they were rewarded with grains of earth-colored salt. This salt they mixed with hickory ashes and rubbed on their meat.

Farmers who lived near the ocean or near salt springs loaded wagons with pans, syrup kettles, wash basins—anything to boil brine in—hitched up a mule team, and started off to make their own salt. They built makeshift furnaces of rocks held together with clay. While slaves chopped wood and kept fires going, they boiled the briny spring or ocean water and loaded the salt into sacks.

Roads leading to a salt spring or to the seashore were jammed with wagons—until the government began impressing wagons and mules for military use. Some luckless farmers returned home on foot, without wagons, mules, or salt.

The most welcome wedding present to a new bride about to set up housekeeping in the South was, as you might suppose, a pound of salt!

WOODFIN OF SALTVILLE

One of the South's unsung heroes was a man named Woodfin, superintendent of the South's largest salt works at Saltville, Virginia. History does not tell us much about him, but he must have been a man of determined character.

When the war began, Woodfin prepared to step up salt production at his works—and immediately ran headlong into one frustrating problem after another.

Unable to get iron kettles for boiling brine, he made vats out of rock and brick. When sacks to pack salt in and twine to tie them became short, he learned to make barrels. Feeding his workers was another problem. Corn that he ordered in April was undelivered in December because the military commandeered the trains for war supplies. So he bought land and began growing corn.

To keep his furnaces fueled and the vats boiling, Woodfin needed wood. By January 1863, a cord of wood was priced at two and a half bushels of salt, and salt cost $22–$25 per bushel. At these inflated prices, he could

Interior view of the Confederate salt works at Saltville, Virginia. *The Library of Congress*

afford to keep only two furnaces going, each of which required twenty-five cords a day.

By November, he had stripped the surrounding countryside for five miles in all directions of every tree and twig. The army came to his aid then by releasing teams and wagons to haul wood from greater distances, but the drivers never reported for work. Those drivers he could hire worked a few weeks, then quit. At harvest season they simply deserted. By Christmas 1863, he had only eleven wagons.

Desperate for fuel, Woodfin built three flatboats to haul wood by water—only to see them seized by the army for shipping war supplies.

Despite these problems, Woodfin somehow kept the works producing salt at the rate of 7200 bushels per day. Farmers and meat packers from as far away as two hundred miles sent drivers and wagons to buy it. But even a busy day saw only 2400 bushels leave Saltville.

Because no trains were available to haul it, Woodfin watched as piles of salt gradually built up around the works. By January 1864, he had stockpiled a hundred thousand bushels. "I doubt," he said despairingly, "if a million dollars will produce a fair train and two cannot be had!"

Here Woodfin put his finger on the heart of the South's salt problem: transportation. While salt shortages caused civilians to suffer and lost the Confederacy tons of meat and leather, salt piled up at Saltville because trains were not available to move it.

Occasionally, when a train could be found, states argued like spoiled children over using it. Tennessee, for example, charged Georgia $900 per car to ship salt from Saltville over its tracks; regular freight brought only $180 per car. In 1864, Virginia billed North Carolina $2000 per day for a train, plus a service charge for the use of tracks and fuel—a total of $24,000 on eight cars of salt from Saltville to Danville, North Carolina.

The states argued that "foreign trains" would wear out tracks, injure roadbeds, and disrupt regular traffic. But, behind the scenes, it was probable that greedy speculators were again at work. With fistfuls of money, these unprincipled men—coldly disregarding the South's war effort and the suffering of her civilians—made secret deals for trains and shipped salt to markets where it could be sold for $70–$80 per bushel.

FIGHTING FOR SALT

While the South struggled with the problems of salt production and distribution, the Union Army added to its woes by harassing Confederate salt works whenever possible.

One by one, the larger works fell to raiding Union troops. In 1862, a vast underground store of salt was discovered on Avery Island, Louisiana. Yet it gave the South no help. The next year, the Union Army captured the island.

By December 1864, Saltville remained the only major salt works left to the South. Then, on December 21, four thousand Union soldiers fought 1500 Confederate defenders in a fierce thirty-six-hour battle and destroyed the works. They burned buildings and smashed furnaces, kettles, engines, pumps, and other machinery. Into the wells they rammed cannon shells, spikes, and railroad tracks. All told, the raiders destroyed a hundred thousand bushels of precious salt and left the works in smoking ruins.

While the Union Army attacked Confederate salt works on land, the Union Navy searched for salt works the South had set up all along the seacoast from North Carolina to Texas.

Hundreds of Confederate salt works edged these shores. The larger ones were capable of producing five hundred bushels of salt a day. Hastily put together with whatever materials were on hand, many of these camps used harbor buoys cut in two to make 150-gallon kettles in which to boil sea water.

The Union Navy detailed shallow-draught gunboats to hunt down these works and destroy them. Gunboats mounted with howitzers and manned by marines cruised the numerous bays and lagoons along the coast until they spotted the telltale smoke of a camp.

While the salt makers fled into the woods or swamps, the marines took axes and sledge hammers and broke the kettles and furnaces. They fired sheds, wagons, and fuel piles, and slaughtered mules and oxen. The salt, they poured into the sand or shoveled back into the water.

On one seven-mile stretch of Florida coast, a Union raiding party consisting of five officers and fifty-seven men destroyed 198 works. Another party, in ten days along a ten-mile stretch of Florida beach, destroyed five hundred works including seven hundred buildings and a thousand kettles.

But it was a battle the Union Navy never won. The salt makers always came back. On one bay, works destroyed in December 1863 were operating again the following February.

In late 1864, the Confederacy set up a Joint Committee on Salt to regulate the production and distribution of salt.

But by then, it was far too late. Before the committee started to work, the war ended.

CHAPTER 5

Pans, Pots, and Wells:
Man Learns to Make Salt

Before he began to raise crops, early man existed primarily on the flesh of animals. He may also have eaten fruit, but his basic food was meat. When he learned to farm, he also gained the benefit of a varied diet.

Up to the time man began farming, about fifteen thousand years ago, the salt his body needed came from the meat of the animals, birds, and fish he ate. He may have felt that cooked grains and vegetables lacked the satisfying flavor of meat; they did not have the same appeal to his taste. When and how he discovered that salt could enhance the taste of cooked food is not known. But discover it he did, and from then on he began to hunt salt to use with his meals.

Men who lived along the seashore scraped salt from rocks at the high-tide mark and from the bottoms of dried up pools of sea water. Those who lived inland followed the trails of animals to salt "licks"—brine springs around the edges of which salt had "candied"—and to salt swamps where salt lay crusted just under the water's surface.

Early man did not sprinkle salt on his food as we do today. As he ate, he was probably content to lick a lump of salt, the same damp salt he had scraped off a rock and packed into a ball, or broken from a crust in a swamp.

He may even have made a kind of "salt sucker." Noticing one day some salt encrusted on a log floating in a swamp, he drove a stick into the swamp's floor. Then, when salt had crystallized about the stick, he pulled it out. At meals, he licked his salt-stick like an all-day sucker. Sticks clustered with solidified salt have been found in caves occupied by early man.

Not long ago, archaeologists exploring a Belgian cave found pieces of clay pots in which early man had cooked wheat and barley. Stuck to the fragments were grains of salt. The scientists fixed the date of the pottery at 3000 B.C., the earliest date known at which man added salt to food.

Other discoveries have established that about 1300 B.C. Egyptians salted quail, duck, and sardines, and the Trojans ate fish preserved with salt.

Driven by his need for salt, man the world over tended to settle where salt was available. In North Africa, Spain, Asia Minor, and parts of South America, he dug it out of salt veins rising to ground level. About such a vein in Arizona, men gathered into a community long before Columbus discovered America.

By the Dead Sea, near the city of Sodom, man found a hill of salt, chunks of which he chipped loose with a stone axe. This hill was named Mount Sodom. Some of the world's earliest known farms developed around the heavily salted Dead Sea.

Man also settled near the Mediterranean Sea—the Minoans evaporated sea water in shallow clay-banked "pans" on the shores of Crete five thousand years ago—and along the great sea rivers that flowed inland.

In Europe, he found salt springs. Some of these springs contained very little salt. Salt makers kept caldrons boiling constantly to get even a thin scraping of salt after the water had evaporated. Year after year the fires blazed under the pots. In some parts of Europe, whole forests were cut away for fuel.

Salt makers in Austria heated rocks in wood fires, then poured on salty stream water. After the water sizzled away, a few grains of salt stuck to the rocks. These grains they carefully brushed into an animal-hide pouch.

Pliny the Elder roamed the ancient world about the Mediterranean Sea and recorded the sights he saw in a thirty-seven-volume encyclopedia. Like other early naturalists, he believed salt was "born of the sun and the ocean."

In one dry area, he marveled over a lake "dried up by the heat of the summer sun, and the whole of its waters, which are at no time very deep, not higher than the knee in fact, are changed into one mass of salt . . ."

"On the shores of Egypt," he observed, "salt is formed by the overflow of the sea upon the land, already prepared for its reception . . . It is made here, also, by the waters of certain wells discharged into salt-pans . . ."

Moving on to Arabia: "Here we find the city of Gerra, five miles in circumference, with towers built of square blocks of salt." Another early traveler recorded observations on these "houses of salt, the walls of which, when they are wasted by the heat of the sun, are repaired by copious applications of sea-water."

SORCERY AND TEN
THOUSAND WELLS

Visiting the town of Changlu, Marco Polo described how the Chinese in that district made salt. "A kind of earth is found here," he wrote, "which is exceedingly salt. This

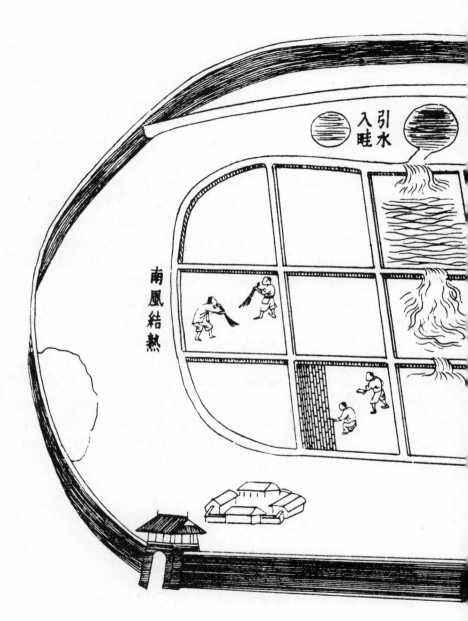

An ancient Chinese solar salt operation shows three steps, top to bottom, in separating salt from sea water. Fresh sea water enters the top pond and flows into the bottom pond, after evaporation, as saturated brine. Workers in ponds at right break up clusters of salt and

carry the salt to a storage pile at lower right. Solar production of salt was used in China four thousand years ago; the process is still used in America today. *East Asian Library, Columbia University*

they dig up and pile in great heaps. Upon these heaps, they pour water in quantities till it runs out the bottom; and then they take up this water and boil it well in great iron caldrons and as it cools it deposits a fine white salt in very small grains. This salt they carry about for sale to many neighboring districts and get great profit thereby."

Near the seashore, Chinese salt makers used a different method to make salt. In winter, they dug pits twenty feet deep. Across these pits they laid bamboo poles. Then they covered the poles with two mats and spread sand over the mats. Each morning and evening, as the tide went out and came in, concentrated salt "liquor" filtered through the sand and mats and dripped into the pits.

In summer, the salt makers descended into the pits with torches to test the brine. If vapor from the brine extinguished the torches, it was salty enough for the next step—lifting the brine out of the pits with buckets and pouring it into clay-bottom evaporating ponds. When the water evaporated, workers raked the salt into one corner of the pond where it drained until ready for market.

Along the seashore, salt makers also sun-dried clumps of seaweed, boiled it, then evaporated the brine to get the salt.

Among early civilizations, the Chinese were the only people who developed a method for removing salt from deep underground. To do this, they combined practical engineering with sorcery. A strange combination, but it worked.

To locate a site for a salt well, a geomancer—one who divined what was under the earth's surface—went through an elaborate ceremony. By use of figures, lines, symbols, and mysterious rituals, he pointed to a spot and announced, "Drill here!"

Exactly how he selected a site is not known, but he

was right often enough. Chinese engineers followed his directions and drilled wells seven hundred to fifteen hundred feet deep. The deepest known well was three thousand feet deep—twice as deep as the Empire State Building is high.

The drill rig for these salt wells was crude, but remarkably effective. It was made almost entirely from China's native plant, bamboo. Bamboo fiber made the rope; bamboo poles with the hard joints bored out made pipes which resisted the corrosion of salt brine.

The drill itself was a length of bamboo tipped with an iron bit. It was suspended from a huge beam or "spring pole." Workers ran up a short incline and walked out onto the beam until it lowered to the ground. The weight of the men raised the end of the beam attached to the drill, like a playground teeter-totter.

"Hai!" the foreman cried, and the men stepped off. The beam swung down and plunged the bit deeper into the earth. As the drill bored deeper, more bamboo pipes were added to the original pipe. Some wells took four years to drill; others as long as forty years!

Medieval travelers to China reported ten thousand of these patiently dug wells. Hand pumps raised the brine from shallow wells. Some kind of mechanical pump, probably powered by oxen, drew it up from wells over seven hundred feet deep. The brine was boiled in iron kettles on mud furnaces.

Salt wells were developed in China about 400 A.D. The brine was
pumped to the surface through hollow bamboo pipes. Notice the
notched end of the pipe in the well and the notched end of the pipe

竹木下

the workmen at left are carrying. The two will be joined together to extend the pipe deeper into the earth. Some of these wells were three thousand feet deep. *East Asian Library, Columbia University*

FABLED TIMBUKTU

One of the chief trade centers for salt in the ancient world was the fabled city of Timbuktu. Located on the southern edge of the Sahara Desert, the city thrived on profits from the salt trade.

Twice each year, merchants sent caravans of two thousand camels accompanied by guards and attendants 450 miles north to the salt swamps at Taodeni. Native workers waded waist deep into the briny waters. With poles, they broke the salt that had crusted on the bottom and loaded the chunks into three-hundred-pound sacks, the maximum weight a camel could carry. Then the caravan made its way back to Timbuktu and its bustling market.

The salt trade made the city prosperous; in Africa, salt ranked with gold and slaves in value. For merchants to risk camels over hundreds of miles of burning sand, the profits must have been enormous. Nor did the city squander its wealth. Timbuktu's salt trade supported schools and libraries; merchants lived in fine houses; the king paid handsome salaries to judges, doctors, and clerics—all from profits on the three-hundred-pound salt cargo that each camel carried.

THE RISING SEA

With the rise of the Roman Empire in the first century B.C., salt making became a major industry in Europe. Evaporating ponds dotted the shores of the continent from the North Sea south around the Mediterranean. Caesar's

A sixteenth-century woodcut shows a seaside salt operation in Europe. Sea water was admitted through a sluice gate (c) into a brick evaporating pan (d). Cells (e) within the pan held sea water at various stages of evaporation. When the salt in one cell had dried, it was shoveled out onto the ground. A small gate in the cell was then lifted to admit fresh sea water. Packed into casks, the salt was then loaded into ships (background) for shipment. *The Bettmann Archive*

"salinators"—salt makers—alone made a million tons of salt a year from seaside salt works.

Then an incredible thing happened which destroyed this industry: the ocean began rising. By 500 A.D., it had risen more than six feet, creating a new shoreline far inland. It had covered evaporating ponds and salt marshes and all the flat, level ground where salt could be produced along the seashore.

For Europe, this rise in the sea level caused—as Belgian historian Henri Pirenne put it—an "economic dark age." Their ponds drowned under six feet of water, salt makers deserted the coasts. Merchants, alarmed at the loss of business, began looking for new sources of salt. Eventually they turned to the Near East where salt was dug from mines far from the coast and harvested from inland salt lakes like the Dead Sea.

In the sixth century A.D., these European merchants began sending ships loaded with gold and marble to the ports of Palestine. On the rich profits from the salt trade, small fishing villages grew to be cities with populations of a hundred thousand or more. For a few hundred years these cities grew fat on the European salt trade.

But the sea was about to change man's fortunes again. From its high-water mark in 500 A.D., the ocean began receding again until, in the tenth century, it had dropped to its old level, and Europe again began making salt on its uncovered seacoasts.

BLACK CRUSTS OF SALT

The early English made what was probably the crudest salt of all.

When Julius Caesar landed in Britain with his armies

in 55 B.C., he found salt makers along the coasts making salt by splashing sea water over red-hot embers in a fire, then scraping off the black crust that formed and using it for salt.

Caesar must have been appalled by the barbaric salt-making methods of the Britons. With his army, he carried his own salt makers; they showed the backward islanders how salt was made by professionals in the Roman Empire: by boiling salt water in open lead pans.

For the early English, the Roman system worked so well that salt making became England's first industry. Wherever a brine spring was located, the English set up pans and production began.

In a history of early England, a writer named William Smith described how these places took names. "The house in which the salt is boiled," he wrote, "is called the *wych-house*. You can guess what *wych* signifies and why all those towns with salt-springs are called by the name of *wych*." These towns exist today, among them Woolwich, Norwich, Harwich, and Sandwich.

English salt makers learned, over hundreds of years, to improve the quality of their salt. Grain size, they discovered, varied according to the heat of the fire over which the brine was boiled. By simmering the brine, they produced kernels of salt; by boiling it, fine grains.

They learned that the white of an egg, or a jelly made from boiled cows' hoofs, would clarify brine by drawing scum to the surface where it could be skimmed off. They tried using forged-iron pans but found that brine corroded the iron. So they continued over the centuries to use the same lead pans the Romans used, the joints of which they sealed with a paste of ox blood mixed with ashes.

Salt was also made along England's southern coast. Sea water was run through shallow trenches into ponds, the water evaporated, and the salt "liquor" was boiled in kettles. By 1086—about the time Westminster Abbey was started—nearly 1200 salt works were operating along this coast.

As their production mounted, the English began exporting salt to Europe. On their way to a seaport, pony packtrains carrying sacks of salt crossed the Thames River at a low-water ford. In spring, when floodwaters made the ford too deep to cross, the ponies had to wait. To protect their valuable salt during the wait, merchants built a fort that later grew into a village called Westminster, the heart of London today.

Dutch, Flemish, and German "salters" on the shores of the English Channel and the North Sea developed the same pan-and-kettle-boiling and sea-water-evaporating methods for making salt as did the English. And like the English *wyches*, German towns beginning with *hal* signified salt-producing springs. Hallein and Hallstatt were two such salt centers.

In Europe, salt was one of the most important chemicals of the Middle Ages. Craftsmen used it in combination with other materials to clean gold, prepare leather, solder the joints of pipes and gutters, set dyes, make soap, and glaze pottery.

OPPOSITE:
A European brine-boiling operation in the Middle Ages. The lead pan is fired with straw, stacks of which are piled at left. As the master salt maker ladles salt into wicker baskets, an assistant places them against a wall to drain. Tools of the salt maker include a spade, hoe, and rake. The tankard containing beer (p) and the two buckets (o) holding ox blood were used to clarify the brine by bringing impurities (including straw ashes) to the surface where they were scooped out. The salt maker's wife is seated in the foreground. *The New York Public Library*

A—Wooden dipper.   B—Cask.   C—Tub.   D—Master.   E—Youth.   F—Wife.
G—Wooden spade.   H—Boards.   I—Baskets.   K—Hoe.   L—Rake.   M—Straw.
N—Bowl.   O—Bucket containing the blood.   P—Tankard which contains beer.

Physicians used it in a variety of remedies—to soothe toothache, relieve upset stomach, and ease mental depression.

For food merchants, it was essential to preserve meat slaughtered for winter food and to store that staple of the medieval dinner table, fish.

In Western Europe, both peasants and nobles ate enormous quantities and varieties of fish: whale, sturgeon, mackerel, lamprey, haddock, eel, cod, and herring, to name a few. Salt was necessary to preserve the fish until eaten. During Lent, breakfast in noble households—for every member of the house, from servant to child—consisted of a dish of white herrings or sprats, bread, butter, and beer. All these foods required salt before they were placed on the table.

UNDERGROUND BALLROOMS

In Europe, rock-salt mining began in Poland and Rumania. About 1000 A.D., a mine shaft was sunk two hundred feet at Wieliczka in Poland. Today the mine is still in operation with five levels going down a thousand feet.

The mine today is as much a tourist attraction as it is a mining operation. In the upper three levels, a visitor can view altars, chapels, and complete scenes from the life of Jesus carved nearly three centuries ago from solid rock salt. He can dine in a salt-walled restaurant and take a rope-guided boat across a lake seven hundred feet underground. He can visit two ballrooms, the result of forty years of excavating salt. These ballrooms are illuminated by six salt-crystal chandeliers and graced by salt statues of Vulcan and Neptune. In the nineteenth century, visitors were even treated to an underground display of fireworks in this amazing mine.

Rumania never lacked miners for its rock-salt mines. The miners were convicts, sentenced to serve their prison terms at slave labor for the state.

In the mine, each convict selected a tombstone-sized square of floor and, with pick and scoop, dug a five-inch-deep groove around it. Then he and his partners inserted the points of their picks into the groove and pried up the slab. Then they pounded the slab into chunks, and the chunks were hauled to the surface.

In the mine, soldiers guarded the convicts. Discipline was simple and effective. For any disobedience, the guards cried, "Drop!" A convict who did not heed the warning to fall flat was instantly cut down by a hail of bullets.

Convicts once staged a sit-down strike. At the end of the work day, they refused to leave the mine until their grievances were heard. They were undoubtedly surprised when the soldier-guards made no effort to force them out at gunpoint. Instead, the soldiers left them in the mine. Two days later, tortured by thirst from breathing the salt-laden air, the convicts surrendered for the promise of a cup of water.

AMERICAN EXPLORERS

When the Lewis and Clark Expedition reached its farthest westward campsite, just inland from the Pacific coast near the Columbia River, the men built a 50-foot-square log stockade.

On January 5, 1806, Captain Meriwether Lewis recorded in his diary that the expedition's hunters had killed an elk and several deer. The hunters then asked the Clatsop Indians of the area for salt so they could store the meat. The Indians, Lewis wrote, "brought with them a specimen of the salt of about a gallon. We found it excellent, fine, strong, and white. This was a great treat to myself and most of the party, having not had any since the 20th of the last month."

Long before colonists arrived in America, salt was being mined by America's first settlers, the Indians. In Nevada and Arizona, Indians dug galleries into the sides of mountains. With foot-long digging sticks shaped like *J*s and stone picks, they chipped away rock to follow thin salt veins.

A few years ago archaeologists explored these galleries, some of which were three hundred feet long. The Indians used no timbers to support their excavations, but simply followed the salt vein into the mountain, picking away at the rock and throwing it behind them. Dead fires and discarded cedar-bark torches indicated how they illuminated their work inside the mountain.

When colonists landed on America's shores, they turned to the sea for salt. In 1635, Samuel Winslow began boiling sea water in kettles on the coast of Massachusetts and received a patent—the first issued in America—for a salt-making method that had been used for thousands of years. His production: seventy pounds of salt—one bushel—from 250–300 gallons of sea water.

The salt that Winslow and other salters produced on the New England coast enabled the American colonists to begin trade with England. Fish and furs the colonists had in plentiful supply. The fish were split open, covered with salt, and stacked in layers in the hold of a ship. Furs were salted and bundled in bales. Sent home to England, these items were traded for manufactured goods the colonists were unable to produce.

THE·PLACE·OF·THE·BIG·BONES

In 1739, Captain Charles de Longueil, commander of Fort Niagara, went on an exploring trip down the Ohio River. Indian guides had promised to show him The-Place-of-the-Big-Bones, a bog where women from their tribe made salt.

The bog was in a small valley near the river. There Captain de Longueil saw a startling sight. In the bog and around its edges, he found skulls and skeletons of animals that no longer walked the earth: mastodons, musk oxen, and mammoths. Some tusks were eleven feet long. He found teeth weighing ten pounds each. The beasts, coming to the bog for salt, had become mired in its ooze. They bellowed and thrashed, but only sank deeper until the water stifled their cries.

Just sixteen years after Captain de Longueil sighted the big bones, an incident took place at this site which altered the history of salt making in America. But the story starts four hundred miles to the east, in Virginia.

On a Sunday afternoon toward sunset, a young woman in her twenties was walking in the quiet of her garden. Her husband, a planter, was away inspecting his crops. Mary Draper Ingles was content. In her arms she carried her first child and, in a few days, she was expecting her second. And then, in one terror-filled moment, her entire life changed.

Leaping from behind trees surrounding the garden, thirty Shawnee braves seized her and her child and carried them off. Mary had time for only one scream.

When the Indians rejoined the main band, Mary found

her sister-in-law, Betty Draper, a captive, too. What followed was a nightmare for these two young women.

They started on a journey that took them four hundred miles west to Kentucky and Ohio. Two nights out, Mary gave birth to her second child. The birth over, the braves placed her on a horse and the journey continued.

Near the present location of Charleston, West Virginia, the party stopped at a buffalo lick to make salt. Mary and Betty were put to work. The Indians unstrapped a kettle from a packhorse. While the braves kept logs burning, Mary and Betty filled the pot with brine from the lick. They stirred the brine and ladled out salt which they packed damp into deerskin sacks.

Down the Ohio River the party went and, at The-Place-of-the-Big-Bones, stopped again to make salt. That night, Mary's new baby cried. A brave, angered at the child's wailing, snatched him from Mary's arms, swung him by the ankles, and smashed his head against a tree. Mary and the other women sat in stunned silence. Would her first child be killed, too? But the brave, his rage satisfied, let him alone.

After three months with the Indians, Mary escaped. One night, with several German women the Indians had captured in the Shenandoah Valley, she crept out of camp. Forty days later, having existed on roots, berries, and fruit, she made her way home to Virginia. At once, men set out with a rescue party, found the Indians, and returned with Betty Draper and Mary's first child.

Despite her ordeal, Mary did not forget her salt-making experience. She returned to the buffalo lick with a party of men and showed them how the Indians had boiled brine to get salt. Up to this time, colonists had obtained their salt through the slow process of boiling sea water. Now they had rich brine to boil.

The place took a name, Buffalo Lick, which was later changed to Saltville, and here Woodfin labored mightily a century later to produce salt for the Confederacy.

The brine at Buffalo Lick rose from a salt deposit 175 feet thick and two hundred feet down. In area, the deposit spread over five hundred acres. In 1800, a salt maker named William King sank a shaft to the deep springs and, from thirty-two gallons of boiled brine, made a bushel of salt—America's first commercial salt production from a brine well.

So valuable was this deposit that, a year later, leases were selling at Saltville for a fabulous $12,000 a year. The salt was 99% pure. By 1860, a bushel of salt was being made from only eighteen gallons of the rich brine.

Like *hal* in Germany and *wych* in England, the term *lick* in America's East came to signify a place where pioneers could make salt. Some of these names exist today: French Lick, Deer Lick, Blue Lick, and Booneslick.

THE BEGINNING OF AMERICA'S SALT INDUSTRY

In 1788, Comfort Tyler, who had been a colonel in General Washington's army, built a cabin on Onondaga Lake in upper New York. Tyler was determined to go into the salt-making business. He had heard rumors of Indians making salt in this area. His one problem was that he didn't know where the salt was located.

One day in May he loaded a fifteen-gallon kettle into a canoe and began paddling along the shore of the lake. Out of the woods stepped an Indian. With sign language, Tyler asked where the salt was located. The Indian stared at him suspiciously; then he nodded for Tyler to follow.

Tyler boosted the kettle onto his head, using his coat for a cushion, and followed the Indian. A few hundred feet into the woods, the Indian pointed to a bubbling well of brine. There was the salt.

That same afternoon, Tyler made fifteen bushels of salt from the rich brine.

Two years later, a salt maker named Nathaniel Loomis arrived at the lake's shore. Using fifteen kettles and working through the fall, winter, and spring, he produced five hundred bushels of salt. He sold his salt for one dollar per bushel.

Next came men who used an assembly line to make salt. At the edge of the spring, they set four thirty-five-gallon pots into a stone furnace. Then they ran the spring water through hollowed-out logs directly into the pots. The brine boiled continuously and the men ladled the salt into bushels.

These pioneer salt makers with their iron pots and stone furnaces were the start of the salt industry in New York.

Pioneers in other parts of the country also began small salt-production operations. The following description of salt making in Kentucky originally appeared in Fortescue Cuming's *Tour to the Western Country 1807–09*. These excerpts are reprinted from *The Register of the Kentucky Historical Society*, LXIV (1966).

"On the clear, cold morning of the twenty-ninth of July (1807), we hauled up our anchor, and dropping down the current three miles [on the Ohio River], we landed at Salt Lick Landing, at six o'clock.

"We walked about a mile to the salt springs. The old, original one, formerly used by the Indians, and another lately opened, are on the west side of Salt Lick creek and are owned by a family of the name of Beal. Three others on the east side of the creek, opened within three years, belong to a Mr. Greenup. The salt is made in three furnaces at Beal's Springs, and in four at Greenup's.

"Each furnace contains 50 cast iron pans, of about 20 gallons each, and makes, on Greenup's side, one hundred bushels of salt per week. . . . The price of salt at the works is two dollars per bushel. A furnace requires eight men to do its work. . . . The water in the old spring is near the surface, but the new wells are sunk to the depth of 55 feet.

"The water is wound up by hand by a windlass, in buckets, and emptied into wooden troughs, which lead to the furnaces. The old spring has two pumps in it. Much labour might be saved by machinery wrought either by horses, or by the water of the neighboring creek; but in so new a country one must not expect to find the arts in perfection.

"The proprietors of each furnace pay a yearly rent of from three to five hundred bushels of salt to the proprietors of the soil . . .

"There is a wagon road of 70 miles from hence to Lexington, through a country settled the whole way. The road passes the Upper Blue Licks, where are also salt springs and furnaces, not nearly, however, so productive as these. The Salt Lick Springs, which are the strongest in this western country, are not half so strongly impregnated with salt as the water of the ocean, yielding only about one pound of salt from 60 pounds of water."

By the early 1800s, salt had become a booming business in the East. In Pittsburgh, where wagons brought salt over the Allegheny Mountains from New York, a pioneer was shocked to see salt priced at ten dollars per bushel, but he paid it anyway.

In 1825, the Erie Canal opened. Called the "ditch that

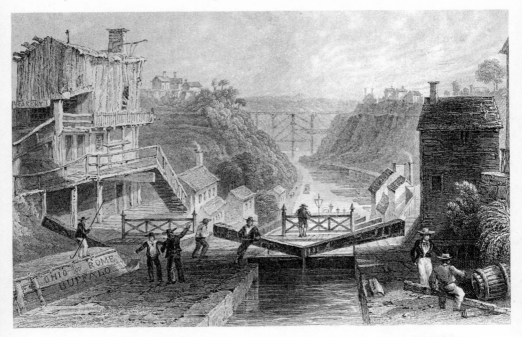

The Erie Canal, along which salt-laden barges were towed by horses, was called "the canal that salt built." *The Library of Congress*

salt built," it carried flatboats of salt west from Troy on the Hudson River to Buffalo on Lake Erie. There the salt was reloaded onto lake boats en route to Chicago with its rapidly expanding population. The canal passed through Syracuse and consequently, with the means of shipping salt at the front door, salt production in that city soared to one million bushels a year by 1828.

Solar production of salt—the evaporation method—began in 1820 on San Francisco Bay. Within forty years, eighteen companies crowded the bay's eastern shore. Chinese coolies worked the ponds. They raked the salt into fifty-foot piles where it was allowed to drain for several months. Then it was bagged and sent to market.

In August 1847, just a few weeks after Brigham Young

and his followers arrived in Utah, the Mormons found salt six inches deep caught between sand bars at the edge of the Great Salt Lake. It was, wrote one Mormon, "as pure, white, and fine as the best that can be bought in the market." Delighted at their discovery, they shoveled it into wagons and headed for their new settlement, their worries about an adequate salt supply ended.

Within the next twenty years, America's rich underground deposits of salt were discovered—in Michigan, Louisiana, Kansas, and Texas—mostly by crews drilling for oil and gas. Down to these deposits men sank shafts and began removing the salt with picks and shovels and hoisting it to the surface. These operations signaled the start of America's rock-salt industry.

THE INDUSTRY'S FIRST

IMPROVEMENTS

Although man had been making salt for thousands of years, he had never improved on his three basic production methods: solar evaporation in ponds, boiling salt brine in kettles, and hacking rock salt out of the earth.

Then, in the 1880s, two American salt makers, Joseph Duncan of Silver Springs, New York, and Crockett Mc-Elroy of St. Clair, Michigan, developed the first advances in salt production ever recorded.

Duncan had been a salt maker for years before he discovered a way to improve on the gray, flaky salt then produced. He found that, by boiling brine in a seven-foot-wide sealed kettle from which air had been evacuated, he could make salt in clean white cubes, like granulated sugar. Duncan discovered that heat combined with low air pressure broke salt down into its basic crystal form, a cube.

His system had another built-in advantage: it used less fuel than did open-kettle boiling. Because water boils at a lower temperature in the thin atmosphere of a partial vacuum, it requires less heat and fuel.

Duncan's method, with more elaborate "kettles" and pumping systems, is the process used today to produce the salt we use on our dinner tables.

Crockett McElroy discovered a way to extract salt from deep underground without digging a mine shaft down to it. He became convinced—after surface salt streams had begun to run dry at St. Clair, about forty miles north of Detroit—that underground streams flowed beneath the town. Like the Chinese fourteen centuries earlier, he planned to sink a pipe to these hidden streams and pump the brine to the surface.

In March 1882, he began sinking a test well. Week after week, the drill bit deeper, but no salt water appeared.

Then, on July 8 with the shaft at 1633 feet, McElroy found salt—and the biggest disappointment in his life.

"Rock salt!" he cried, examining the flakes and crystals on the drill tip.

McElroy's hopes vanished. He realized there was no way to extract salt from that depth except by digging a mine shaft, sending down men, and pick-and-shoveling it out.

McElroy brooded over the loss of his dream. Then one day as he sat staring at the pipe that plunged a quarter-mile into the earth, he suddenly saw the solution to his problem.

"If there is no salt water underground to pump up," he told himself, "then I'll send water *down* to the salt!"

Quickly he assembled a narrow pipe, lowered it through

the first pipe, then pumped water down between the two. Just as he expected, the water dissolved the rock salt, and rich brine gushed back up the inner pipe. He was mining salt from deep within the earth without even seeing it!

Today, McElroy's brine-pumping method accounts for over half the salt produced in America each year.

CHAPTER 6

How Man Produces
Salt Today

If all the thirty-six million tons of salt America produced last year were loaded aboard sixty-ton boxcars to make up a single train, the train would be nearly five thousand miles long. With its caboose in New York City, the train would reach to Portland, Oregon, and back again to New York.

The United States is the world's chief producer of salt, and has been since 1897. Fifty-seven companies in eighteen states account for three out of every ten tons produced throughout the world today, more than the next three countries—China, Russia, and England—combined.

Seven states (Texas, Louisiana, New York, Ohio, Michigan, California, and West Virginia) produce 93% of the total U.S. output. Louisiana, America's major salt producer, accounts for more than three times as much salt as all the countries of South America.

SALT MAKING AROUND THE WORLD

Although the world's salt production continues to rise each year by about nine million tons—world production is now 125 million tons a year—man continues to hunt for salt in various corners of the globe.

Recently, Australian oil drillers discovered a 1544-foot-thick bed of salt a mile and a quarter underground.

In Chile, a company began surface mining operations on a seven-thousand-acre dry salt lake. The thickness of the deposit, geologists found, varies from a few feet to nearly a thousand feet.

The first South African plant for solar production of salt began operation in mid-1964 at Goega near Port Elizabeth.

UNDER LAKE ERIE

The newest rock-salt mine in America was opened in 1962 in an unusual location: under Lake Erie. When guides tell visitors, "You are now under Lake Erie," everyone suddenly looks up, but all they see is the mine's salt ceiling.

Developing a mine today involves problems that pioneer salt makers never encountered. The salt bed, a part of the Great Eastern Salt Basin, actually extends under Cleveland. But it was far more economical for the salt company to acquire mineral rights from the state of Ohio for the salt under Lake Erie than it was to deal with hundreds of property owners for the salt under their homes in Cleveland.

The mine entrance, a shaft sixteen feet in diameter, is located on Whiskey Island, one and a half miles from downtown Cleveland at the mouth of the Cuyahoga River.

The deposit lies nearly 1800 feet below the surface of Lake Erie. Although the bed is forty-six feet thick, only the middle fourteen to seventeen feet will be removed from the 5100-acre reserve the company has leased from Ohio. The reserve holds about a hundred million tons of salt and will require anywhere from fifty to a hundred years to mine at the estimated production rate of one to two million tons each year.

STILL A LUXURY

Despite new sources of salt, new plants, and increasing salt production, salt is still a luxury for much of mankind. To get the salt they need, people in many countries today produce it by methods their ancestors used centuries ago.

In the Pyrenees Mountains between Spain and France, the villagers of Gerri—a community of sixty families—make salt at the same mountain spring their forefathers used.

Through hollowed-out tree trunks their salty spring water flows into *salinas,* or salt pans, about fifteen feet to a side. After the sun evaporates the water, the villagers sweep up the salt and store it in an eight-hundred-year-old warehouse. A summer's harvest provides two thousand tons of salt.

Greeks on the island of Rhodes still extract their salt from the ocean. Using four-gallon tins, the islanders pour sea water into shallow volcanic craters on the shores of their island.

In five days the water evaporates. Then island salt makers gather the damp salt and spread it in the sun to dry for three days before taking it to market.

Along Venezuela's coast, salt makers have built a system of canals through which ocean water is admitted to evaporating pans. They harvest the salt by stamping on the salt crusts and then loading the broken chunks into baskets.

In the interior of Africa, salt crystallizes on the sandy banks of the Congo River. To refine it, African salt makers pack both salt and sand into baskets made of twigs and leaves. Then they pour boiling water through the baskets

In Bolivia, men hack salt out of the Salar of Uyuni just as their Inca ancestors did between the thirteenth and sixteenth centuries. A dry salt lake twelve thousand feet high in the Andes, the Salar is said to be larger than Switzerland. *Black Star*

OPPOSITE:
Bearing hundred-pound sacks of salt, Guajira Indian women of Colombia walk across broad salt beds during the annual salt harvest on the Guajira Peninsula. Leaving their cattle and sheep ranches,

more than two thousand Indians and their families take part in the harvest. The salt has been evaporating for ten months under the hot tropical sun. Gathered into eighteen-hundred-pound mounds, it is carried to shore by the Indian women for commercial and domestic use. For each bag, an Indian is paid about ten cents. In use since the sixteenth century, these salt beds yield about forty-two thousand tons per year. *United Press International*

to dissolve the salt. The sand stays behind on the leaves. They boil the salt water, then pack the salt into clay jars for use or for trade.

In Thailand, families own sections of salt-bearing streams. They make their salt by splashing brine on sun-heated rocks and scraping off the salt after the water has dried.

In 1954, an explorer traveling in the interior of New Guinea saw how some of the most primitive people on earth make salt in a way that has been passed on for generations.

These simple people, who wear loincloths and pierce their noses with bones, produce salt under conditions that, in more modern countries, would require elaborate chemical equipment.

In a gorge of the Wahgi River, a village sits on the banks of a salt-bearing stream flowing from a mountainside. The stream, however, is not pure brine. Mixed with the salt is sulphur. Yet these primitive people, driven as all men are by a need for salt, have developed a way of removing the sulphur from the brine to make, if not pure, at least edible salt.

First they soak grass in the sulphurous brine. Then they spread the grass in the sun to dry. The drying grass, the explorer recalled, gives off an odor like manure.

They burn the grass, now impregnated with both salt and sulphur, place the ashes in a bark funnel, and pour water through it. The water dissolves the salt and leaves the sulphur behind in the ashes.

The brine is then boiled, and the salt scraped from the sides of the kettle and packed into molds made of flat stones ridged with clay. When the salt has dried, the clay is broken away. It takes two weeks to produce one "pancake" of salt.

In the dense forests of New Guinea, these pancakes of

A New Guinea tribesman holds pancakes of salt still in their clay and stone molds. *Arnold Maahs—Black Star*

salt are enormously valuable. In trade with other villages, one pancake will buy a small pig or such a luxury as a plume from a bird of paradise.

SALT MAKING IN AMERICA

Three methods are used in America today to produce salt: it is dug out of mines as rock salt, pumped out of deep wells as brine, and evaporated from sea water.

Rock-salt mines are usually located six hundred to two thousand feet underground.

"Back to the salt mines" is a popular saying that makes many people think a salt mine is a horrible place to work. Not so. If you would tour a salt mine, you would find it safe and comfortable. The temperature remains a steady, autumn-like fifty-eight degrees. Filtered air, pumped down from the surface, blows gently through the broad corridors.

Salt mines are free from the natural hazards miners face in coal mines. No explosive gas hides in concealed pockets; no faults in the salt overhead threaten the collapse of the ceiling. Nor does water drip from the ceiling in a salt mine. Moisture in the earth reacts with the salt to form a crust about the entire deposit and this crust seals the mine's interior from seepage.

To remove rock salt from deep within the earth, salt companies use the "room and pillar" method of mining. Corridors wide as a four-lane highway are the rooms from which salt has been removed. They are usually fifty to sixty feet wide and nearly as high as the salt bed is thick—anywhere from eight to twenty-five feet in most mines. To keep impurities out of the mined salt, a foot or two of salt is left on both the ceiling and the floor.

The pillars are usually sixty-by-eighty-foot columns of

solid rock salt left standing to support the hundreds of feet of overburden between the mine's ceiling and the earth's surface. In a coal mine, timbers support the roof of a narrow tunnel from which the coal has been removed. Coal, compared to salt, is soft; it collapses under great pressure. But rock salt is so hard that no support other than these pillars is necessary. Its ability to support weight is about twice that of brick.

A room and pillar mine spreads over a broad underground area, like an underground city. Under Detroit, Michigan, for example, a salt mine in operation since 1910 covers a square mile and has sixty miles of corridors.

Salt mines, especially those out of which salt has been extracted for many years, extend for miles underground. Miners ride to their work stations in trailers. *International Salt Company*

The Western Hemisphere's largest salt mine, the Retsof near Rochester, New York, covers 1600 acres underground. One thousand feet down, the mine contains rooms sixty-three feet wide and five hundred feet long. The pillars are fifty-seven feet wide and from 185 to 220 feet long. About 70% of the salt in the nine-and-a-half-foot-thick seam is removed. The remainder is left in the supporting pillars.

Each room ends at a "face" of salt where the actual digging operations go on. At the end of each day's work, a corridor will have advanced another ten feet through the earth.

MINING UNDERGROUND SALT

All machines used in the mining operation are first taken apart on the surface and then carried down, piece by piece, on an elevator to the mine floor. There, in a modern machine shop, they are reassembled for use. The machine shop also makes repairs on broken equipment.

The first step in mining rock salt is called undercutting.

An electrically powered machine that resembles a chain saw on wheels cuts a slot six inches high and ten feet deep into the salt face at floor level and across the entire room.

This slot is cut across the bottom of the face for two reasons: to keep the mine floor level, and to allow for expansion when the salt is later blasted loose from the mine face.

A drilling rig then replaces the undercutter at the mine face. It drives up against the face and four high-speed drills, long as vaulters' poles, bore sixty holes eleven to thirteen feet deep into the face from floor to ceiling.

Powder men load these holes with an explosive and attach wires to blasting caps.

The caps are set to go off at intervals measured in thousandths of a second. The bottom holes go off first and drop the salt into the six-inch slot along the floor. The next shot drops the salt into the cavity created by the first blast, and so on up to the ceiling. So rapidly do the blasts follow each other that the entire sequence of shots, from floor to ceiling, lasts less than one second.

In undercutting, a chain saw on the nose of this machine cuts a slot into the mine face at floor level. The horizontal black lines in the salt wall are impurities—usually shale and limestone—which processing will later remove from the salt. *International Salt Company*

After the blast, power shovels move in and load the salt
—about 780 tons per blasting—into twenty-two-ton tractor-
trailers. The tractor-trailers, headlights on, rumble along
dark corridors and dump the salt into a primary crusher,
the first of a series of crushers that grind the blasted
chunks of salt to pebble size.

Step two in preparing a room for blasting: drilling holes for explosives
into the salt face. *International Salt Company*

The crushed salt travels on conveyor belts to storage piles. About two hundred thousand tons may be stored underground for later hauling to the surface.

The room and pillar method of mining rock salt is horizontal in direction. But salt-dome mining along the Gulf of Mexico is both horizontal and vertical. Rooms in salt domes reach heights of seventy-five to one hundred feet.

Step three in preparing a room for blasting: an explosive powder is poured into each hole and the holes are wired for firing. *International Salt Company*

A tractor with a front-end bucket piles the blasted salt. Note water vapor leaving the exhaust pipe at the tractor's rear. A special filter called a "scrubber" removes poisonous carbon monoxide from the exhaust. *International Salt Company*

An electrically driven power shovel loads the salt into a bottom-dumping tractor-trailer. *International Salt Company*

OPPOSITE:
Salt leaves the primary crusher in chunks no larger than eight inches in diameter. *International Salt Company*

A conveyor belt carries salt to an underground storage pile. Two conveyor belts are used when the salt must turn a corner on its way to storage. *International Salt Company*

An underground storage room. This salt has been run through a series of crushers. It is now the size of marbles. The black specks in the salt are crushed impurities which will be removed before the salt is hauled to the surface. *International Salt Company*

A "room and pillar" mine under Detroit. In the main corridors, tractor-trailers run on power from overhead trolley wires. The photographer lighted the "rooms" along the corridor to take this picture. But mine corridors are unlighted. Tractors use powerful headlights to find their way along the black corridors. *International Salt Company*

A salt "dome" mine in a southern state. The ceiling in this mine is a hundred feet high. In the background is a self-propelled work platform. *International Salt Company*

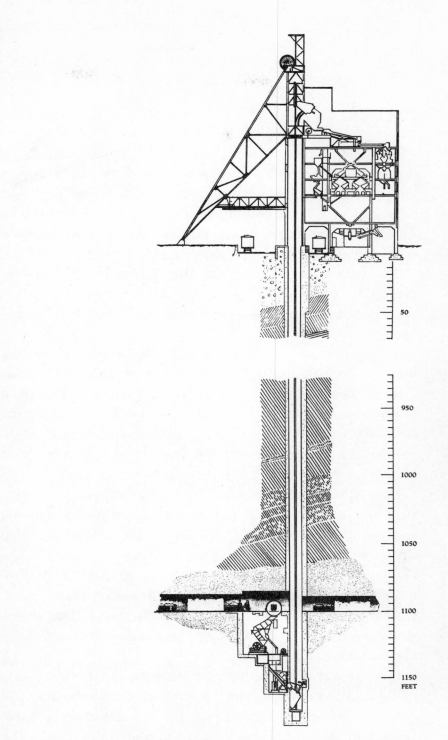

Cross section of a rock-salt mine. The shaft penetrates layers of sand, clay, shale, and limestone to reach the salt deposit. After the salt is mined and crushed, it is hoisted up the shaft to the surface. *International Salt Company*

BRINE WELLS

Pumping salt from wells, called "hydraulic mining," is the simplest method of removing salt from deep underground deposits. Salt wells are sunk 750 to a few thousand feet deep by oil-well drilling rigs. The deepest brine well in America is located in West Virginia on the east bank of the Ohio River. Its depth: 6800 feet.

The brine-pumping method that Crockett McElroy invented in 1882, in which he used two pipes, one inside the other, has since been developed into a more advanced operation.

Two pipes are still used, but the pipes are spaced five hundred to a thousand feet apart. Water under high pressure is pumped down one pipe and drives through a fault or a fracture in the salt bed until it reaches the second pipe—called the "target well"—which draws it to the surface at the rate of 2.65 pounds of salt per gallon of brine.

Hydraulic mining requires elaborate pumping systems. In a single day, twenty million gallons of water may be pumped into a well and 850 thousand gallons of brine drawn out.

Because of the enormous quantities of fresh water required, brine wells are usually located near rivers or lakes. One of America's major hydraulic mining operations draws water from the St. Clair River as it flows between Lake Huron and Lake St. Clair.

One company in California is experimenting with a new method of hydraulic mining. Superheated water is pumped down a well under tremendous pressure. When the brine returns to the surface, it instantly flashes into steam. The

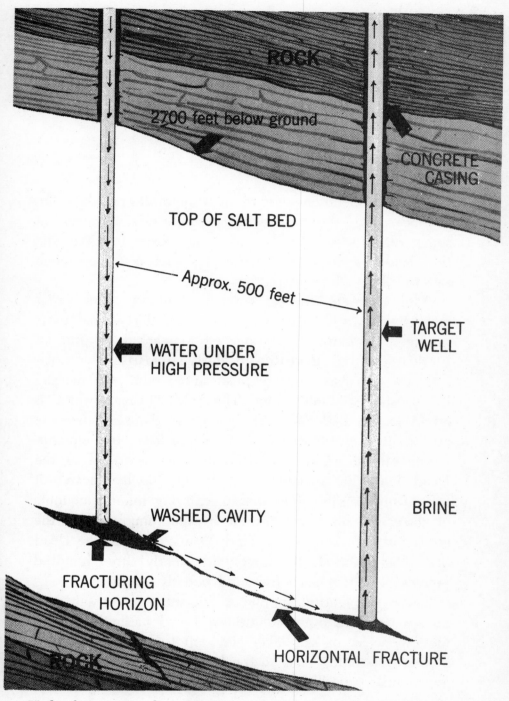

ROCK

2700 feet below ground

CONCRETE
CASING

TOP OF SALT BED

Approx. 500 feet

WATER UNDER
HIGH PRESSURE

TARGET
WELL

BRINE

WASHED CAVITY

FRACTURING
HORIZON

ROCK

HORIZONTAL FRACTURE

Hydraulic mining: diagram of a modern brine well. *International Salt Company*

steam passes into the air, leaving the salt behind. Should it succeed, this experimental method promises to short-cut the costly piping system in today's hydraulic mining operations.

SOLAR SALT

Solar salt operations require great quantities of salt water. The oceans are the most plentiful supply of salt water, but some inland seas, like the Great Salt Lake in Utah and the Dead Sea between Jordan and Israel, contain enough salt to allow solar salt production.

Oddly enough, the salt content of ocean water varies around the world. The Atlantic carries thirty-three parts salt to a thousand parts water off Massachusetts. But off Florida, the salt increases to thirty-six parts. The polar seas are the least salty because snow, rain, and melting ice constantly dilute them. The saltiest ocean water is found in the Red Sea—forty parts per thousand—because of the high evaporation rate of water near the equator.

The saltiest water on earth, however, is found in the Dead Sea. This ancient body of water is landlocked; it has no outlet. The River Jordan, carrying minute amounts of dissolved salt, flows into it. Evaporation removes the water but leaves the salt behind. Year after year, the Dead Sea gets saltier. Today it contains nearly three hundred pounds of salt in each thousand pounds of water.

Besides a plentiful supply of salt water, solar salt production requires other conditions: broad flatlands bordering the ocean or salt lake; clay soil to seal the bottoms of the evaporating pans so the brine cannot seep through; low annual rainfall to prevent dilution of the brine; and steady sunshine.

The largest solar salt production center in the United

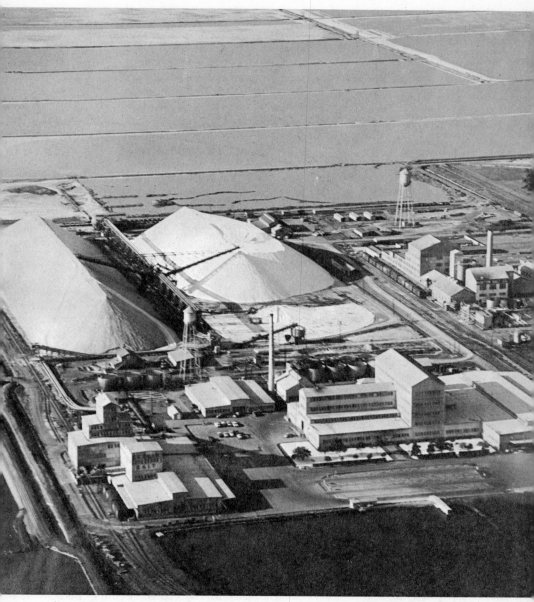

Aerial view of a modern solar evaporation plant on the shores of San Francisco Bay. At the top of the picture are shallow ponds—some of which are eight hundred acres in size—into which sea water is admitted for evaporation. Stockpiles of salt are at center. *Leslie Salt Company*

Solar evaporation of salt. Brine flows through a sluice gate, past crystallized chunks of salt, into a garden pond. *Morton International*

States is located on San Francisco Bay. Here one company operates evaporating ponds spread over fifty thousand acres along the bay's southeast shore. These ponds produce over one million tons of salt each year.

The climate in the San Francisco Bay area approximates desert weather conditions in the dry spring and summer months and, for solar salt operations, is nearly ideal. Trade winds blow seven months of the year, aiding evaporation. And steady sunshine evaporates water at the rate of thirty-four to forty-three inches annually. Sea water gives up about one inch of salt for each six and one-third inches of water evaporated.

Solar salt production requires three sets of ponds: concentrating, garden, and harvest ponds.

In spring, sluice gates are opened, and sea water flows into concentrating ponds about five hundred acres in size. Since San Francisco Bay water is only about 85% as salty as ocean water—because fresh water empties into the bay from the Sacramento and San Joaquin Rivers—water is taken into the concentrating ponds only at high tide when the ocean flows into the bay.

After some of the impurities have settled, the brine is released to the intermediate garden ponds. Averaging sixty acres in size, the garden ponds allow further evaporation of the brine before it is drained, heavy with salt, into the harvest ponds, the final step in producing solar salt.

Forty acres in size, harvest ponds have hard-packed clay bottoms. The temperature of the brine may reach a hundred degrees as the sun evaporates the last of the water. By September, salt lies clustered in the harvest ponds to a depth of five or six inches.

Between September and December, when the rains begin, tractors scrape up the wet salt. It is hauled away in railroad cars rolling on temporary tracks laid on top of the salt. The harvest ponds then remain empty until the following April when the concentrated brine from the garden ponds again flows into them and the cycle of salt production by the sun is renewed.

A solar salt operation requires about fifteen acres of concentrating and garden ponds to each acre of harvest pond.

Close-up of salt in a crystallizing pond ready for harvesting. Salt averages five inches in depth. *Leslie Salt Company*

Harvesting solar salt. A narrow-gauge railway has been placed along-side the tractor's path. When the tractor reaches the end of the pond and starts a new sweep, the tracks will be moved to parallel the tractor's path until the entire pond has been scraped clean. *Leslie Salt Company*

PROCESSING SALT

Raw salt, whether it is evaporated from ocean water or pumped or mined from the earth, always contains impurities. But solar salt is purer than either rock salt or brine pumped from wells; only about a half-pound of impurities remains in each hundred pounds harvested.

The amount and kind of impurities left in the salt after refining varies according to the use of the salt. Bits of calcium sulphate mixed in salt, for example, will harden canned peas. Butter makers require salt at least 99.4% pure; salt with a higher percentage of impurities will give off a bitter taste in butter.

Removing impurities like shale or limestone from rock salt (amounting to about three pounds in every hundred mined) was a problem until recently. In 1960, the salt industry developed a separation process to remove these troublesome impurities speedily and efficiently from tons of rock salt.

Researchers found that salt is transparent to infrared heat waves, while impurities mixed with the salt absorb infrared heat. This is how the impurities are removed from tons of rock salt mined each day:

The raw rock salt passes through a drum on a conveyor belt. Within the drum are infrared heat lamps. The lamps heat the impurities, but the salt remains cool because the heat waves pass through it. At the end of the drum, a chute carries the salt and its heated impurities onto a revolving resin-coated belt. The warm impurities stick to the resin, but the salt flies off the end of the belt into a bin. The impurities are then scraped off into a waste bin.

Stockpiling solar salt. Tractor-trailer in background delivers salt to a hopper. A conveyor belt carries the salt from hopper to blower. *Morton International*

The purest processed salt, however, is produced by the vacuum-pan method, a refinement of Joseph Duncan's invention in the 1880s.

Today, in place of the single vacuum pan Duncan used, salt manufacturers line up four pans in a row. These giant sealed pans resemble two cones joined together rim to rim. They are nine to twenty-four feet in diameter and sixty to seventy feet high, about as tall as a six-story building. A set of four vacuum pans can produce five hundred tons of salt in one day.

Pipes from brine-storage tanks keep brine flowing evenly into each pan. There it is agitated violently by a propeller and boiled by steam.

In the first pan there is only a low vacuum. The steam boils the brine and passes on to the second pan. In this pan, a slightly higher vacuum is maintained to compensate for the heat loss of the steam passing into it from the first pan; thus the brine boils at a lower temperature than in the first pan. By the time the steam has reached the fourth pan, the vacuum is so high that the brine boils at only 120 degrees, nearly a hundred degrees less than the temperature at which water normally boils.

In each pan, salt crystals sink to the bottom where they are pumped away as slurry—wet salt.

The slurry flows to heated, revolving drums which remove most of the moisture. The semi-dry salt then moves into rotating ovens that tumble it and bake out every last trace of moisture.

OPPOSITE:
Inside these vacuum pans, live steam boils salt brine. These pans produce granulated salt that is 99.99% pure. This is the salt we use in salt shakers with our meals. *International Salt Company*

The completely dry salt, now 99.99% pure and in the form of granular crystals, is then screened into various grain sizes depending upon the use to which it will be put. This is the salt that appears in salt shakers on your dinner table—with one addition.

Salt used in the home has a "free flowing" agent mixed into it because salt attracts moisture and moisture cakes salt so that it clogs in the holes of a salt shaker.

This chemical agent must perform an astounding variety of jobs—and all at the same time. It must absorb moisture; it must stick to each grain and cover it completely, yet not so completely as to cut off the taste of the salt. It must be nontoxic, odorless, colorless, dustless, tasteless, inexpensive, and soluble. Finally, it cannot react chemically with salt. Some chemicals that fill the bill and keep our table salt flowing freely despite humid or rainy weather are magnesium carbonate, calcium silicate, and calcium carbonate.

GRAINER SALT

Food processing companies that can vegetables and creameries that make butter and cheese use vacuum-pan salt almost exclusively; it is the purest salt available.

But there is yet another process in use today for making salt. Although less than 2% of the salt produced in America is made by the grainer method, this method was the chief way to make salt a century ago for the canning and dairy industries.

In 1833, George H. Patrick of Onondaga, New York, developed the grainer method. He used a long shallow pan into which brine flowed continuously. The pan was heated by wood fires. As the water evaporated, Patrick raked up the salt crystals as they settled to the bottom. The pans became known as "grainers" because the salt crystallized into grainy flakes.

Today, while the principles of producing grainer salt have not changed, the equipment has. Pans are two feet deep, twelve to eighteen feet wide, and a hundred to 120 feet long. A large grainer can produce ten tons of salt per day. Pure brine flows steadily into the pans and is heated by steam-fed coils just below the surface. The individual salt crystals collect into flakes that sink to the bottom where automatic rakes sweep them along over one end of the pan.

By altering the temperature of the steam, flakes of varying sizes can be made—as fine as talcum powder to mix in pancake and cake flour, pinhead-size for pretzels and crackers, or thin soft flakes for use in making cheese. By the early 1960s, however, the highly productive vacuum pan had largely replaced the grainer.

CHAPTER 7

Fourteen Thousand
Everyday Uses

Most people associate salt with food, with sprinkling it on meat and potatoes. But this accounts for only a small part of the salt produced in America each year, five out of every hundred pounds.

Amazing as it may seem, those other ninety-five pounds are divided among fourteen thousand other uses. It is safe to say that, without salt, modern civilization could not survive.

Fortunately, salt is inexpensive. If it were rare and costly, like gold or uranium, our country could not maintain its high standard of living because nearly all the material goods we use owe their existence, somewhere along the line between raw material and finished product, to salt.

In its chemical form of one atom of the metal sodium and one atom of the gas chlorine, salt is the lifeblood of the chemical industry; the major consumer of salt, it uses sixty-six out of every hundred pounds produced.

Of the 150 most important chemicals used in America today, salt is required to produce 104, exceeded only by sulphur which is used in 120. Some of the important chemicals in the production of which salt is used are: sodium, chlorine, caustic soda, sodium sulphate, sodium carbonate, hydrochloric acid, sodium bicarbonate, sodium nitrate.

In its pure state or broken down into its sodium and chlorine parts to make other chemicals, salt was used in the manufacture of nearly every item you can see about you at this moment.

The paper these words are printed on was bleached with salt. If you happen to be sitting at a desk, the wood out of which it was made was cured with salt. The window through which the sun is shining was made with salt.

The fabric in your trousers or skirt was cleansed in a salt solution. The thread holding your clothes together was strengthened in another solution. Salt made the colors in your blouse or tie fast so they won't run. Salt prevented the leather in your shoes from decomposing before they were manufactured.

The list of products using salt in their manufacture is nearly endless: synthetic rubber tires, plastic combs and toothbrushes, dynamite, brass and bronze, soap and detergents, aluminum, color TV, paint, cheese and butter, varnish and wallpaper, toothpaste and scouring powder, the lacquer finish on your family car.

Salt is used to harden steel in gears and plows, soften water, bleach fabrics, sweeten the naturally bitter taste of chocolate, glaze tile, tan leather and hides, preserve meat and canned vegetables, cure bacon and ham, refine gold and silver, kill weeds and insects, make ice cream, extinguish fires, remove fruit stains from tablecloths, and treat burns, toothache, bee stings, and tired feet.

Salt purifies water and sterilizes sewage. It makes ice in refrigeration plants and, in winter, melts it from streets. It grows molds for antibiotics like Aureomycin. It refines crude oil into gasoline. It removes dandruff and cools nuclear reactors.

Salt helps to cure hides. Hides are stacked flat and covered with salt in the ratio of one pound of salt to one pound of hide. *Morton International*

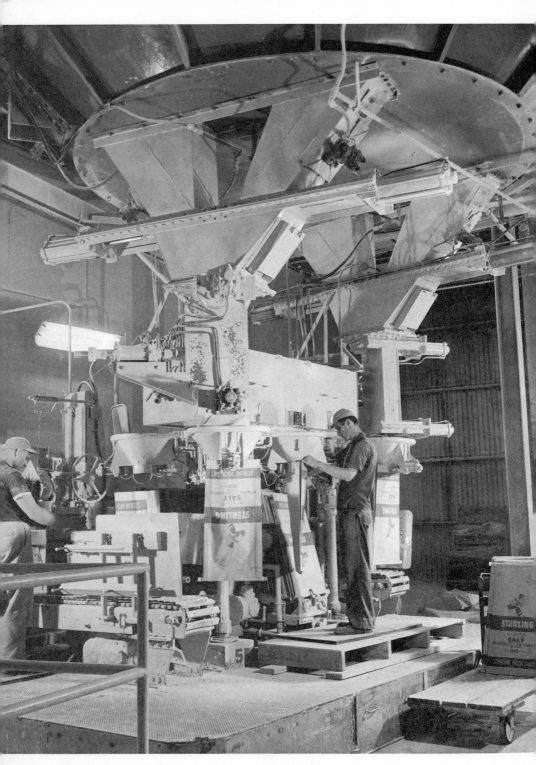

One-hundred-pound bags of salt are filled and stitched at the rate of twenty-eight per minute. The salt flows into the bags from the huge storage hopper at the top of the photo. *International Salt Company*

SALT VERSUS GOITER

Salt provided the key to one of man's great triumphs in public health.

In Michigan in the 1920s, medical authorities were faced with a major health problem. As many as two persons in five were disfigured with goiter, an ugly swelling of the throat. In severe cases, the goiter grew as large as an orange or grapefruit. Among 32,000 school children examined, nearly half showed symptoms of this disease. Even stray dogs had swollen throats.

U. S. Public Health Service doctors investigated the problem and soon found the answer. Goiter developed when people lacked an essential chemical in their systems: iodine. In Michigan, farm soil lacked this vital chemical. Vegetables, fruits, and grains grew without it, and thus people did not get it in their diet. Goiter resulted when the thyroid gland began swelling in reaction to the lack of iodine it needed to function normally.

Doctors had found the solution, but now they faced the question: how could you treat an entire population threatened with goiter?

Salt provided the answer they needed.

Public health officials asked salt makers to add iodine to table salt in the ratio of one pound for every ten thousand pounds of salt. Everyone ate salt, they reasoned. Thus everyone—an entire population—could be treated to prevent goiter. This is the salt that today is labeled "iodized salt."

So successful was salt as a carrier for iodine that goiter vanished as a public health problem in Michigan.

"Even mongrel dogs roaming city streets now have normal thyroids," remarked one doctor.

Salt in public health. Adding iodine—a goiter preventative—to table salt. As salt passes below on a conveyor belt, iodine in solution sprays on it at the rate of one pound per ten thousand pounds of salt. *International Salt Company*

MYSTERY OF THE CROOKED CALVES

In the early 1960s, farmers in some western states were baffled when their cows began giving birth to "crooked calves." This deformity in their stock—bent legs, twisted spines, and necks—cost them millions of dollars each year.

By 1963, researchers at Washington State University were investigating the mystery. Normal calves, they discovered, had two to three times as much manganese in their bones and tissues as did the deformed calves.

On some older farms, years of farming and erosion had removed vital minerals from the soil. The grains and grasses growing on these farms therefore lacked those minerals— iodine, iron, and manganese among others—that cattle, sheep, and pigs required for healthy growth.

With their findings on hand, the researchers sought the help of salt companies. By adding manganese to the salt they sold to western farmers, salt makers helped solve the mystery of the crooked calves.

As early as 1850, a French researcher observed that sheep which were fed salt grew fast and healthy, whereas those that lacked salt in their diet had rough coats, lost weight, were less lively, and produced weak or dead off- spring.

Today, researchers know that all animals, both on farms and in the wilds, depend on salt, just as man does, for health and for life itself. When denied it, some animals become cannibals: sows eat their own piglets and hens peck their chicks to death for the salt their flesh contains. When they added salt to the drinking water of their hens and pigs, farmers found that cannibalism disappeared.

In 1947, scientists from Cornell University observed a

herd of cows deprived of salt in their feed. The cows developed what the scientists called a "depraved appetite." To get the salt their bodies needed, they licked urine, manure, and dirt from the floors of their stalls. They even licked the sweat-stained overalls of the farm hands who attended them.

One cow became so weak on her salt-free diet that she sank to the floor exhausted. She could neither eat nor drink. A veterinarian tested her body temperature: it was six degrees below normal. "She'll be dead by morning," he pronounced.

Animals require salt just as man does. A salt block impaled on a stake offers livestock a convenient way to get salt. *U. S. Department of Agriculture*

That night, the scientists fed her a quarter-pound of salt. By morning, a remarkable change had come over her; she was standing, eating her feed, and drinking from a pail. Her eyes were bright. Within a few days, she had recovered completely.

An experiment at the Kansas Agricultural Experiment Station in 1949 showed that steers fed salt as part of their normal diet gained a half-pound in weight each day while those denied salt gained only two-tenths of a pound.

Salt for livestock is pressed into fifty-pound blocks by a hydraulic press. *International Salt Company*

There is a story about the farm-store clerk who grew tired of stacking salt blocks outside the store each day for sale to farmers. Wondering how he could get out of the heavy work of piling the fifty-pound blocks in a neat display, he suddenly hit on a bright idea. Quickly he lettered a sign and propped it in front of the piled blocks. Within two days, every salt block was sold.

The sign read: "In memory of the cow who died for want of salt!"

SALT BUILDS ROADS

Salt is a valuable aid to highway transportation. It helps build roads and, in winter, it keeps them free from snow and ice. Next to the chemical industry, road builders use the greatest amount of salt in the United States, thirteen out of every hundred pounds.

Salt is the cheapest road deicer known. It bores into the ice and undercuts the bond between ice and road. The ice becomes loose and riddled with holes; it is then easy to scrape up. One pound of salt will melt over three pounds of ice at minus six degrees Fahrenheit. At thirty degrees, one pound will melt forty-six pounds of ice.

In the 1920s, an American construction firm in Greece was building a road. Heavy trucks driving over the road raised clouds of choking dust.

As an emergency measure, workmen tried to settle the dust by dousing sea water on the road—and made an important discovery. To their amazement, they found the dust remained settled even when the water dried. Since then, salt has been used in the construction of highway roadbeds in America.

A ship unloads rock salt for future use in ice control on city streets.
Salt Institute

A roadbed is made of clay, sand, gravel and stone.
When wet, it is compact. But when the moisture evaporates,
the roadbed dries and crumbles.

Salt mixed throughout the bed, road makers learned, re-
tains the moisture which holds it together. Without salt,
a highway could hardly absorb the pounding of millions of
wheels each day. Beneath its hard concrete surface, the
roadbed would crumble and the concrete would eventually
collapse.

Adding salt to a road under construction. *Salt Institute*

RESEARCH AND DEVELOPMENT

Has man exhausted all possible uses for salt?

A salt company executive answered the question this way: "The salt industry is, of course, interested in new uses for salt. However, it's unlikely that dramatic new large-tonnage uses, like road de-icing, will be discovered."

But salt companies continue to search for new uses for their product. Some salt companies maintain research and development laboratories. Besides discovering new uses, these laboratories have other goals: to search for more efficient and economical ways to produce salt from mines, wells, and evaporating ponds, and to find out more about the physical and chemical properties of salt.

Recently, one company developed a new flake salt which is now being used in a variety of ways. Light, thin, irregularly shaped crystals of 99.5% purity, these flakes have a surface area fifty times greater than granulated salt— and dissolve five times faster. Their weight is only fifty-five pounds per cubic foot, compared with seventy-six pounds for granulated salt. This new salt has already found use in metal polish, in sweeping compounds, in shampoo and hair rinses, as a dental-plate cleanser, baking-dough conditioner, and as a color-setting agent in dyes.

Some other matters currently being researched in the laboratories of American salt companies are: salt's effects on high blood pressure; its value as a carrier of drugs to control intestinal parasites in farm animals and as a carrier for vitamins; its use in an anti-malarial salt for tropical countries and a fluoridized salt to prevent tooth decay; the shape of salt crystals that gives the most rapid melting action for ice control; ways to remove impurities from salt; and ways

to detect and remove minute quantities of rare metals
found in salt.

SALT AND RAIN

Man has learned to use salt to meet many of his needs;
research promises even more uses. But perhaps the most
remarkable new use for salt may be to make rain.

In recent years, oceanographers have come up with a
surprising discovery. Released from the sea and drifting
about in the air are minute particles of salt which help to
make rain. These invisible specks of salt are carried on the
wind inland from the sea. They come from minute bubbles
flung into the air at a great speed from waves cresting at
sea or from surf crashing onto a beach. The bubbles evaporate, leaving particles of salt to ride the wind.

Depending on its speed, a good wind can carry ten to a
hundred pounds of salt in a cubic mile of air; storm
clouds may carry as much as a thousand pounds.

Above and near the sea, the air is filled with salt.
England, surrounded by ocean water, averages a salt-fall of
twenty-four to thirty-six pounds per acre per year. British
Guiana on the northern coast of South America gets a
hundred pounds per acre per year.

But what has this to do with rain?

Salt has a natural affinity for water. On rainy days, we
sometimes see salt shakers become clogged as the salt
draws moisture from the air. Salt particles drifting in the
air also suck up moisture. They are among the many bits
of matter in the air, like dust, about which moisture col-
lects to form raindrops.

A salt particle about the size of the period at the end of
this sentence will produce a raindrop the size of a pea.

A particle the size of a single buckshot will absorb enough moisture to grow into a raindrop with the diameter of a marble.

Will man one day be able to produce rain at his command by spraying salt into the air from an airplane?

The idea still requires study and experimentation. But salt has already proved an excellent vehicle to absorb moisture from the air and turn it into rain. Perhaps the only thing lacking is the man to make this yet-new use of salt a practical venture, one which is no more incredible than the thousands of other uses man has found for salt.

WATER BANKRUPTCY

Salt may be the key agent in a problem that is threatening America's future prosperity: water bankruptcy.

In 1961, a Senate committee investigating America's growing water shortage reported this: "We face a water crisis that threatens to limit economic growth, undermine living standards, endanger health and jeopardize national security. We live on the edge of water bankruptcy!"

America's water, once considered an inexhaustible natural resource, is beginning to trickle out.

In 1900, a small U.S. population used only forty billion gallons of water a day. By 1940, that figure rose to 135 billion gallons. In the following twenty-five years, we more than doubled our demands to 340 billion gallons a day. And one frightening day in the 1970s, our growing population will consume a quantity of fresh water equal to the total flow of rain and melting snow streaming each day into the nation's reservoirs: 650 billion gallons.

The average home in America uses a hundred gallons of water per day per person—to wash clothes, dishes, and the car, to drink and bathe, to sprinkle lawns.

But homes consume less than 10% of our water. Agriculture uses approximately half our supply: it takes 1.6 million gallons to irrigate a single acre of cropland for one growing season or 120 gallons to grow the wheat for a pound loaf of bread.

Industry uses the remaining 40% of our water: 110,000 gallons to produce a ton of steel; 240,000 gallons to make a ton of newsprint; 600,000 gallons for a ton of synthetic rubber; thirteen gallons to brew one gallon of beer.

Loss of usable water through rivers pouring thirteen million gallons a second unused into the sea, leaks in water mains and aqueducts, careless irrigation, and pollution of rivers by sewage and industrial refuse adds to America's growing water problem.

While both state and federal governments are looking for ways to correct these abuses of our water supply, man is now turning his eyes upon the sea as a source of drinking water. Remove the salt and sea water is as useful as water from the kitchen tap.

In mid-1965, President Johnson took a dramatic step which will allow us to drink at least part of our water from the sea. The government, he announced, will spend $185 million by 1970 to build sea water desalting plants for the nation's big coastal cities. Each plant will have the capacity to convert a hundred million gallons of sea water each day into fresh water. The funds will also provide a number of ten-million-gallon plants by 1968 for smaller cities.

Removing salt from sea water to get fresh water is not a new idea. Aristotle, the Greek philosopher, wrote that "salt water, when it turns into vapor, becomes sweet, and the vapor does not form salt water again when it condenses." During the siege of Alexandria, Julius Caesar's soldiers boiled sea water and converted the steam to fresh water.

Today, man is learning to desalt sea water on a mass

production basis, and this may eventually be the answer to our growing water shortage. Two hundred desalting plants around the world, nine of them in the United States, are busy converting fifty million gallons of fresh water from sea water each day.

The world's biggest complex of desalting plants is located in the oil-rich but water-poor sheikdom of Kuwait on

Sea water desalting plant, Guantánamo Bay, Cuba. Serving the U.S. naval base in Cuba, this plant produces two and a quarter million gallons of fresh water each day. *Westinghouse Electric Corporation*

the Persian Gulf: four plants produce 5.2 million gallons of fresh water each day. Other plants are located in Egypt, Indonesia, Libya, Saudi Arabia, the Virgin Islands, and at the American naval base at Guantánamo Bay, Cuba.

THE "TEAKETTLE" TECHNIQUE

While several processes have been developed to separate salt from sea water, one process is being used most widely about the world. It is called the "teakettle" technique. Heated salt water is sprayed into a low-pressure vacuum chamber. In this chamber, a portion of the water flashes instantly into vapor which is condensed into pure water and piped away. About one gallon of fresh water can be obtained with this process from each three and one-half gallons of sea water. The processed water is so pure that a pinch of sea salt is tossed back in to take away the flat taste.

Another method is just the reverse of the teakettle technique. Instead of heating sea water, the water is frozen. Ice crystals of pure water form, leaving the brine behind. These crystals are washed with pure water to remove every last trace of salt, and then melted.

Other promising methods for desalting water are electrodialysis and reverse osmosis.

In electrodialysis, a current of electricity is passed through a tank of salt water on one end of which is a plastic membrane. The salt filters through the membrane and leaves pure water behind.

Reverse osmosis also uses a plastic membrane. Salt water is forced under pressure against the membrane; pure water passes through and the salt stays behind.

Useful on a small scale, both electrodialysis and reverse

osmosis have not been perfected yet for mass production of fresh water.

"Within the next decade," President Johnson stated in 1964, "desalted water will be the cheapest—and in some cases the only—way to obtain new water supplies in many areas."

By the year 2000, the U. S. Department of the Interior's Office of Saline Water predicts, 7% to 10% of America's water will come from converted salt water. This converted water will come not only from the sea, but also from brackish underground water that threatens to pollute wells supplying at least a thousand communities, most of them west of the Mississippi.

Water that contains one part of dissolved solids per thousand parts is considered brackish. City water, by contrast, contains half as much and is considered safe for human consumption by public health officials. Sea water contains thirty-five parts per thousand.

Buckeye, Arizona, was the first U.S. community to build a desalting plant to convert brackish underground water to fresh. Opened in 1963, the plant gushes forth sixty-five thousand gallons of fresh water each day. Now Buckeye housewives no longer complain about coffee with a salty taste or about scale forming in teakettles and around the bathtub.

Already, industrial giants like Westinghouse, General Electric, and Dow Chemical are building plants and researching ways to make desalted salt water cheaper to produce.

Salt, so useful in so many ways, now promises the bounty of fresh water for the world's growing population.

CHAPTER 8

What of the Future?

About one hundred years ago, the people of North America were convinced that their supply of trees was inexhaustible. So, in the space of about thirty years, the great forests of Wisconsin and Michigan were obliterated. Big trees were cut down and sawed into boards and small trees were crushed by lumberjacks, machines, and by falling trees. No thought was given to conservation, and men moved on— leaving desolation behind them.

About fifty years ago, the people of this continent were convinced that their fertile soil was inexhaustible. So they used the soil, never replenishing its nutrients, never thinking of using the soil wisely. The result was that, by the middle of the 1930s, an estimated hundred million acres had been ruined in the United States alone. Another 125 million acres were in the process of being ruined, and the men moved on—leaving desolation behind them.

Just a few years ago, the people of this continent were convinced that their supply of water was unlimited. But now we are paying for our misuse of water; many parts of this country are experiencing a critical water shortage. According to one scientific estimate, the water supply in the United States is only enough to support about 230 million people, while the census bureau expects our population to pass that mark some time between 1975 and 1978.

Time after time, man has thought that his natural resources were inexhaustible—only to discover that he was rapidly approaching the point of total exhaustion of these resources. Can this be true for salt, too?

It would appear that we truly have an inexhaustible supply of salt. "The reserve of salt in the United States has been estimated at 60,000 billion tons," states the U. S. Department of the Interior's Bureau of Mines—enough salt at today's rate of use to supply all the nations of the world for the next six hundred thousand years! The Bureau concludes: "Conservation [of salt] is seldom considered."

But let us take a closer look. To begin with, more people exist on earth today than ever before. And they all need salt. In 1650, only one-half billion people lived on earth. Two hundred years later, there were twice that number. But by 1920, the population had doubled again to two billion. As you can see, this time the doubling of the population took only seventy years instead of two hundred. Only forty years later, one billion more people occupied the earth. Today, our population of over three billion people has begun to crowd this planet.

At the same time that the world's population is increasing by leaps and bounds, industry is finding new uses for salt. Not only do we have more people who demand salt, we also have more uses for salt than ever before.

Add to this the fact that we are, to some small extent, polluting our present sources of salt—by storing radioactive wastes in salt mines, for example, and by dumping industrial waste into the ocean—and a tiny problem begins to appear. More people need more salt. More industries need more salt. And we have slowly begun to pollute some sources of this precious material.

Despite these small indications of waste and the increased demands on the world's salt supply, we do not think that a shortage will ever develop in the civilized world. However, it would pay us to keep some facts of history in mind. The human race seems to have a talent for destroying its natural resources rather than for using them wisely. Let us, therefore, keep in mind that, while it may not *now* be necessary to conserve salt, we do not want our children or our children's children to blame us for squandering this—our most vital mineral resource.

Author ROBERT KRASKE is also the editor of a weekly magazine for primary-grade children. He grew up in Detroit, Michigan, graduated from Wayne State University, and served in the Army Air Force. His writing has also appeared in *Science Digest*.

Mr. Kraske lives in Kettering, Ohio, with his wife Jan and their three children.

Index